W9-CDE-562

NOON

NOON is an independent not-for-profit literary annual published by NOON, Inc.

Edition price $12.00 (domestic) or $17.00 (foreign)
All donations are tax deductible.

—

NOON is distributed by
Ingram Periodicals, Inc., 18 Ingram Boulevard,
La Vergne, Tennessee 37086 (800) 627-6247

NOON welcomes submissions. Send to:
Diane Williams
NOON 1324 Lexington Avenue PMB 298 New York New York 10128
Please include the necessary self-addressed, stamped envelope.

ISSN 1526-8055
ISBN 978-0-9676211-8-0
© 2008 by NOON, Inc.
All rights reserved *Printed in U.S.A.*

NOON is indexed by *Humanities International Complete.*

Cover photograph by Valerie Shaff/Stone/Getty Images
Interior cover photograph by Comstock/Jupiterimages

CONTENTS

The Editors proudly congratulate Lydia Davis, 2007 National Book Award Fiction Finalist for her collection of stories, *VARIETIES OF DISTURBANCE.* Seven of these stories appeared in previous editions of NOON.

The Editors proudly congratulate Clancy Martin, recipient of the 2008 Pushcart Prize, for his story "The Best Jeweler," which appeared in the 2006 edition of NOON.

The Editors proudly congratulate Rebecca Curtis, whose story "Family Means Nothing to Me and I Dislike Children," which appeared in the 2007 edition of NOON, was reprinted in *Harper's Magazine*, May 2007.

A GROS

IT COULD BE AS MANY AS NINE

DEB OLIN UNFERTH

The idea was to bring the two mothers: The two mothers could help care for the baby. The two mothers could help keep the place clean (rentals dirty so easily). The two mothers never get out to the country. The two mothers could pay (mostly) for themselves.

So that was the idea except, he noticed, they didn't pay for themselves, and they turned out to be of no help. They did clean — too much, under his very feet while he tried to get a few minutes' peace to read the paper, in the very bedroom while he and his wife tried to sleep. No, it wasn't that they wouldn't stop cleaning, said his wife. It was that *one* of them wouldn't stop cleaning, his mother. Yes, he said, she had to because *her* mother wouldn't clean at all. Her mother did nothing but stand in the way with her arms crossed or eat bread over the sink or say loudly how much *his* mother didn't know.

So two mothers, but really, he figured, it was three mothers since technically his wife was a mother. Or four mothers, since one week in, his previous wife showed up to drop off his previous child and then proceeded to stay for days, and days, not cleaning, not paying, instead bossing the new wife, the current wife, around. Picking up the baby and saying, Oh, she's filthy. Don't you ever give her a bath? So that the new wife, the young wife, so young she had hardly gotten past being mothered herself and could herself use a bath, turned to him and said, You tell that wife of yours to put my baby down.

That, and the two eldest mothers, his and hers, argued in the kitchen over soap or dishes or drainers or cups, over food and hair and beds and milk, floors, shoes, sheets, the outdoors, the indoors, the government, the law, men, bags, dust, and war (I, II, and the others approaching). And there were the failures of the younger mothers for the elder mothers to point out, child care, of course, being the worst and at the top, but also thrift, health care, and knowledge in several categories such as geography and books and fashion. So at moments it seemed like two mothers might form a team against the others but didn't.

You tell her, said the new wife about the first wife, to keep her hands off my baby. And also off my suitcase, my clothes, my hair, my man. Hands off.

You're just jealous, said the first wife. You got yours used. He was mine first, so anything that comes from him goes through me first then to you.

Tell her that's not true, said the new wife, the younger, so young she looked like a child, another child and mother he had to take care of.

She was never good at sharing, said a mother who would know. Never could share a toy, she said.

So there were four mothers total, plus his little daughters (potentially two more mothers)—the one from the one wife and the other from the other.

His own mother had never understood him. Even as a child, he had played alone with his Lite-Brite on the floor. His mother had never wanted to be a mother, he believed—but had any of them? he wondered, surveying the group. A piece of them did, a piece of each them wanted to be mothers. But a piece of each of them didn't. Even this new fresh wife, was she, too, showing signs of not wanting to be a mother? Sometimes. And was the elder daughter, at only eight, was she showing signs of it? Maybe. Was the baby? Was even the baby scoffing at him from her little bouncy, not liking, not wanting the role she would one day claim? Perhaps so. Perhaps they all blamed him, which is why they were all standing over there like that.

He had left his first wife for a woman he no longer knew. She had been neither a wife nor a mother. She had flitted off one night, never returned, and was preserved here today only in name, in script, tattooed on his arm.

There were no men other than him. Even the three poodles, shaky and shaken from travel, were female. They did have a bird once, a male, whom he privately named after himself and who died one morning and lay stiff in the straw of the cage.

He went into the kitchen, had been preparing for a drink for hours by now, and they were preparing, it seemed, to find out the things they had always wanted to know:

Did he call that clean?

See how he was?

Was he ready or not?

WORK

BRANDON HOBSON

He began talking about his young wife, who was asleep in the next room. It was late, well after midnight, and I started feeling drunk from the wine. He poured me another glass and told me she wanted to have a baby.

"What do you think of that?" he asked. "Having a baby, at my age?"

"I think you should do it," I told him. "Go have a baby, be a father."

"I'm getting too old to screw."

Our game was near the end. He moved his rook, the only good piece he had besides his king.

"I want to show you something," he said, and got up from the table. He returned with photos and spread them out on the table.

They were photos of his wife, naked. Dozens of them. He leaned over them like a man serious about his work. His wife was sleeping in the next room. Every so often I heard her cough.

THE SINGLE WHIP

BRANDON HOBSON

We sat with my brother in the backyard so he could watch the birds and butterflies. One summer afternoon we read him Russian fairy tales and had a tea party with him.

"He's smiling!" my sister said.

"He's happy to be alive!" she added.

Then, after a while, it began to rain, and we had to go inside. Our uncle was sitting at the kitchen table with his head in his hands. He never said anything to us, just sat there. We tried to talk to him, but he wanted to be left alone.

"Would you like some tea?" my sister said. "Or milk?" she added.

Our uncle rubbed his head. Then, without saying anything, he got up and went to his bedroom and shut the door. We followed him and listened at the door. It was very quiet. My sister knocked lightly and said, "Please come out."

There was no response, so we waited for him, just as he preferred. My sister put her face in her hands and began to cry. Finally, it stopped raining, and the door remained closed. We took our little brother back outside and waited for him to laugh or to cry.

THE BODY BELONGS TO ME NOW

CLANCY MARTIN

"The old bitch cheated me, I believed," Yun said. "The way she lied! She reminds me of my mother. You see I already understand that she is not interested in money. She wants to be rid of it for some other reason. How I guess this I do not know. I am not a clever man, but I get lucky. Nearly I ruin the luck. I am so excited by the bracelet that my mouth is talking on its own. 'It is valuable,' I tell her. 'It is an easy bracelet to sell. But I will have to fix the clasp.'"

"She has to leave it. So you can show it," I said.

"It was not her bracelet to sell," he said to me.

This was a time when, because of my personal romantic situation, and because of my divorce and my two-year-old daughter, I was drawn to stories of hope and fear.

We were in the massage room because you could not talk

in the other rooms, not without being extremely rude. We had picked our girls and paid for the services we had selected: Yun was having only a massage and I was staying on after him for the full treatment. Yun was on his stomach and I was on my back. We were receiving simple Western massages, not the elaborate Buddhist massages that involve pulling on your arms and legs and treating you like a piece of exercise equipment. So we could smile and talk and the atmosphere was nurturing rather than sexual or athletic.

"Are you in a hurry?" I said.

"No," he said. "But I am hungry. I am diabetic, you know, I eat every two hours. Do you need to eat? We eat now. I finish the story at lunch. You come back for the girl after the massage. She does not run away. She is safe," he said. He reached out one hand and pushed the girl toward me from her back. "You tell him," he said.

I was very hungry. I had gained twenty-five pounds since Lucy and I left the States. I thought the depression of homeless-ness would help me lose weight. But quitting the coke again had reversed my metabolism.

"First we finish our massage. You got an orange or something, woman?" he said.

"You want a banana?" she said, and laughed. She went to find a banana over on the other side.

"Here you are, sir," she said. "Here is a banana." She had sliced the banana and placed it on a lovely small blue and white china plate. She placed the plate on a tall stand, like a stand you would place a goldfish bowl on in an entryway, next to the massage table. She had also brought a nice, fresh linen napkin. "Can I get you a water? A coffee?"

"I cannot eat bananas," he said. "They are for monkeys, not for men," he said. "Don't worry, I got a chocolate here in my bag." He hopped, naked, off the table, and crossed the room to where our clothes were hanging. I looked away. "You want some?" he said. He offered me the half-eaten chocolate bar.

"No, thanks," I said. "I am allergic to chocolate." That was not true, but it was a pretense I had fallen into back in my teens because of acne.

"That is bad luck," Yun said. He lay back down on the table. "I have no allergies," he said. "Man, that is good chocolate," he added. "You should try anyway. You never know," he said.

He continued the story. He still had the bracelet. Both in the story, I mean, and in real life. I sensed that, this time, I would own it.

"So I am working on the clasp when she knocks. It is going well. I like this clasp I am making. It is fitting. When I see her I almost do not open the door. But she has seen me already. Her hair was wild. She looked like she slept in the street. 'Did you sleep in the street?' I asked her. I do not know why I asked her this. I think only because I thought it was true."

Then Yun sat up. It was embarrassing to me because he displayed a large erection.

He rose and went to his little red backpack that hung from a hanger next to his suit and tie. He had a great erection, which, on his slender frame, and with his long hair on his shoulders, looked almost like it was the man and he was the shy penis trailing behind it. But then he returned with the jade bracelet. I almost expected him to present it to me on the end of that cock.

He handed it to me. Normally that is a salesman's trick. But not in this instance, I believed. The bracelet was as thick as two thumbs. I lifted it up. I pulled a towel across my lap. Yet when you held it up to the light you could see your fingertips through the stone. No imperfections. Perfectly patterned color distribution. But within the color was every shade from indigo to rose.

"It's like flowers, eh? Evening comes, there is sky. This is the color. Like the old chink! He gets his ladder and chisel and says to his wife: 'I go get it now, for you, the bracelet!' And cuts it down out of the sky."

"So this is not the bracelet?" I asked him.

"What do you think? What do you believe?" he said again.

Then, suddenly, he gave me an Asian look. All the expression was gone from his face. I was fearful to offer the wrong answer. I had never seen that look on his face before. We looked at one another across the jade bracelet in my palm. It was cold — like jade always is. The two women worked our shoulders.

"No," he said. He laughed. "This is the same bracelet. Just to joke. You and me, now we can joke like this! This is the right one. I tease you. Let me tell you it is old enough, Clancy Martin, that no one can say when the stone was cut and polished. It could be four thousand years old. It is jade that has not been mined for centuries and centuries. All this jade is gone into history. It is jade owned by an emperor."

Beneath the pinks you could see the green, hidden like blood in the purple. There was no orange, no white, no yellow. Naturally no brown.

"I collect jade for sixty years and I do not see it."

I started to hand the bracelet back to him, but he waved it away.

"It is no longer my jade," he said. "You buy the bracelet now," he said. "This is my advice to you as a friend."

"What about the old woman?" I asked him.

"Oh, she dies, the old woman. Like my wife."

After that, of course, I knew more was in the story.

"They left the old woman her ring," Yun said. "You should have seen this diamond, Clancy Martin. It was an eight-and-a-half carat emerald cut F, could be E, flawless. Like just from the polisher. The diamond is on her finger. They did not take it. Maybe because it was an emerald cut. You know, no sparkle, it was dirty. It was platinum, the thieves do not know, street gangs, you know, fools, they think it is a CZ set in silver. A costume ring. They could get sixty thousand for the ring but they steal her shoes. Maybe her knuckles stop them! She had those knuckles like rocks old women have. But you want it, you cut off the finger. They would have cut off her finger if they knew what it was."

"The bracelet?" I asked him.

"No, man, the ring! The bracelet was long gone, are you crazy? At first, I say to myself, I know it, she is dead. Someone bashed in the top of her brains. But no, she is breathing. She was lying on the tile, man, next to an empty cigarette machine. I watched her there, and I thought, Look at you, old woman. One day my wife will be old, too, I thought. But no, that was a mistake."

Yun laughed. I smiled but then I looked away, out the window. Yun's wife had recently died of breast cancer, so I did not know if smiling was the right thing to do.

"I bought a brush at the newspaper stand," he said. "I brushed her brittle hair. I lifted her out of the garbage she was lying in onto a bench. She slept. Good, I thought: it is not easy to be old. I rested her head in my lap like she was my wife. Her hair came away in the brush. Her purse was gone. Someone had taken her shoes. I was embarrassed for her because her naked feet looked big for her legs. Are you listening, Martin? Do you understand?"

THIS IS HOW I GOT MY START IN THE JEWELRY BUSINESS

CLANCY MARTIN

I

The story goes my big brother, Jim, was caught dressing up in our grandmother's black Mikimotos when he was scarcely two years old, but the first time I had considered jewelry was the morning I stole my mother's wedding ring. It was white gold — a hundred-year-old Art Nouveau band with eleven diamonds in two rows across the finger, garnets that were sold as rubies in the centers of tiny roses on both sides, and hand-engraved scrollwork on the underside where it held the finger. It was the only precious thing she had left. It was never off her hand. But there it was on the sill of the window, above the kitchen sink, next to a green plant she kept. I needed the money. My girlfriend was leaving me for a grocery-store produce clerk named Andrew, a high school basketball forward, and I knew I could buy her back. So I took the ring and put it in my pocket. I removed the red rubber stopper from the drain so that my mother would believe the ring had flushed into our plumbing. For good measure I ran the water to wash it down. She might be in the other room listening.

I brought the ring to a trusted pawnshop on Seventeenth Avenue, two blocks from my old high school, to sell it to John Strickland. This pawnshop was on the first floor of a three-story building with a barbershop on the second floor and a pool hall on top. We were told never to go into that pool hall. I should have gone to a pawnshop farther from home, but I had not yet learned to reflect in that way. The barbershop on the second floor was called "Henry's" and there were stacks of *Cheri*, *Fox*, *Club Confidential* and other porno magazines on the side tables next to the chairs where you waited. Some men read them while they were having their hair cut. When my little brother and I were kids we were afraid to look at them, then when I was older and went in alone I pretended to be uninterested.

The pawnshop was the authentic kind I would come to love: three jewelry cases with real bargains on Swiss watches and odd antique pieces, mixed in among crap like ten-karat gold nugget bracelets and blue topaz pendants and amethyst rings.

"I know it's not much. It's an old ring, I guess."

"It's not so bad. Let's see what it weighs. Is that platinum? Or just white gold?"

"I don't know. What's platinum?"

That was not a question for the seller to ask.

"I know those are diamonds, though. Those must be worth something."

"Take a look under the loupe. Full of carbon. See those black specks? That's called carbon. That's what it is, too. Carbon molecules that never crystallized. Imperfections. Really hurts the value. Lots of inclusions, too. Lots of internal flaws. But no cracks. That's something. I couldn't touch it if there were cracks. Too risky."

He knew his business. Didn't steam it, didn't clean it at all. We were looking at sixty years worth of dirt, hair, and skin.

He gave me three hundred dollars for the ring, which was about correct. Given his position, that is.

"I hate to sell it. I inherited it, you know. My grandmother."

"I can loan against this," he said. "This is a loan, no problem. Normally I will do better for a loan. But on this I can do better if you sell it outright."

Then I wished I had said it was a friend's. In case he called my parents or something.

"But there's this girl."

"Love is a good reason. The best reason. Think about it. That's why your grandmother left it to you. She didn't think you were going to wear it, did she? No. It was for a girl. If you need to sell it for the girl, that's what she would have wanted. Women understand these things. What matters and what doesn't. You should hear all the love stories they tell me in this place. A pawn-shop is the place to learn about love."

"Your grandmother had good taste in jewelry," he said, after he had paid me. "This won't be here long."

Good, I thought.

Today that ring would retail for seventeen, eighteen thousand, but at that time I imagine it brought three grand. He may even have paid slightly high.

John was not a friend of mine but he had bought several things from me including a heavy walnut box holding sterling flatware I had found in the bureau of another friend's home. In fact, it was not the friend's home but a friend was baby-sitting there, and a few of us got together to steal drinks from their liquor cabinet and watch a video. While the popcorn was popping I wandered into the dining room and found the silver. My friend Tina, the babysitter, came around the corner and caught me. But I had not moved it. I had only opened a drawer. So she could not say anything. She raised her eyebrows at me and said, "Clancy, what are you doing?" I explained that I was looking for a bowl for the popcorn. Before we left, after several drinks, while she was kissing the other friend of mine in a corner, I returned there and hurried out with the silver in my arms. I lost some friends that way. During this time friends did not matter to me. You could not trust them, they were hard to come by, and they were always more work than they were worth.

2

Often, at night, when I was twelve, thirteen, fourteen, and it was winter and the snow was falling, I would leave our neighborhood and climb the hill up into Mount Royal, to walk through their streets and look into the illuminated windows of the houses.

You know what that's like: when it is very cold and still, because the snow is falling straight down, and it hangs in circles in the streetlights, and inside the houses there is calm or happy movement, as though people are eating and laughing, and their lamps by their windows look like gold and jewels. I would listen to the snow under my tennis shoes and fold my arms deeper into my coat. These houses were enormous, three, four, five times the size of ours, with larger cars and larger yards — much larger — and made of stone and brick, but nevertheless they seemed so welcoming, they were very warm places, you could see that easily enough. I knew my father had grown up in a house like one of these. My mother, though, was raised in an apartment. When we were down in Florida at Christmas my father would tell me: "You can have a poverty-consciousness, son, like your mother, or you can have a wealth-consciousness. It's up to you. Some people are determined to be poor. Your mother and that idiot she married. They can't help it." That was one reason I took those walks. To work on my wealth-consciousness.

3

Even with many seasons of practice I have never been good at stealing and when they kicked me out of high school it was stealing again that did it. A case of class rings for the graduating seniors. When I got them to the pawnshop it turned out they were all base-metal counterfeits. Brass and iron plated in ten-karat gold and sterling silver. Nevertheless, Mr. Robinson and the high school security guard tracked me down for it. They had been after me for a year so it was an excuse for them to play detective. I experienced the same enthusiasm and malice later, with the bankruptcy. We were lucky if we saw a hundred grand a piece out of losing the store, but that didn't stop the creditors and customers from tearing after us like rats.

"But they aren't even worth anything," I said. "You cannot expel me because of some fake rings."

"You don't belong here, Clancy," Mr. Robinson said. "This place is for good people. You are not a good person. You are a thief, a liar, and a coward."

Thief and liar I could make sense of, but why would he say coward? It was curious to say that to a sixteen-year-old. He should act like an adult with adult responsibilities. But being a principal is a business for bastards. The old line about principals is they can do the job with one word: no. I associate him now with my ex-wife's divorce attorney and with a different attorney, a bankruptcy expert named Brad Grain, who represented one of my investors in Fort Worth. Robinson was tall and had a bald head. His fingernails were dirty and he had green cuticles.

When I called my big brother, Jim, to tell him about high school he pitched me on the business. I should have known that as soon as the pitch started Jim believed the lies he was selling me. It's like being an actor or the prime minister, you get all worked up with the audience and you think you can say nothing false.

"It wasn't your fault," he said. "The same thing happened to me, more or less, it was just drugs instead of thievery." I did not like the word *thievery*. Then I saw it had a sex appeal. "The problem is being Canadian. It's not Mom's fault either. That's what I'm saying. Move down here. I'll pay for the ticket and you pick it up at the counter at the airport. You and me are first. We lead the charge. Let me handle Mom. I'm making five grand a week down here. That's twenty thousand dollars a month. Plus the company car. A Porsche! Next year I get the convertible. You would live rent-free. I am a gemologist now. You can take the classes, too. Live with us. That's college! You do it in the mail. I'm listening. That's what I'm saying. You don't even need regular college first. You don't even need high school. We will sign you up. You could be a gemologist in a year. You won't believe what those guys make. The real GIA gemologists. That's the Gemological Institute of America. That's better than university, Clancy. We can ride into work together every day. They have the whole package down here. In a few months you can buy your own car. You'll learn the business in no time. You'll be on the counter in a month. I'm the front-of-the house manager. I'm in charge of the sales floor."

"What about my girlfriend?"

"Of course you'll meet girls! You'll meet a thousand of them. Half the sales force is girls. College girls, too. Coeds! You know what they're like. And customers. Girls love jewelry, Clancy. That's most of the market. And women, of course. But lots of girls. You should see the girls! Everybody knows about the girls in Texas. They are the best girls in the whole country. These do not look like Canadian girls. You wouldn't think they were the same kind of animal. I'm telling you. Like in a magazine. You've never seen anything like it. And they love Canadian guys. They love the foreign accent. They are all over us. Dave is coming down, too. You remember Dave. My old partner in the business. Don't talk about it over the phone. You know what I mean. It doesn't matter now. We make more money this way. Ten times as much money! And it's all legal!"

"What I was saying was I met a girl up here. A girl in one of classes. In my old school. I guess she's my girlfriend."

"That's great! I say give it a try. You can have ten girlfriends. Plus you can always go back. Make some real money and fly her down for Christmas. Think of the presents you can buy her. That's another thing. You can buy any jewelry you want. For employees it's all twenty percent over cost. You don't know how cheap it is until you're on the inside. You can buy jewelry for nothing! I had no idea. It's triple key, quadruple key, five times. You'll learn all that when you get here. That is what I explained to Mom. How much you will learn. I'm a businessman now. It is not just selling. It's big business. It's called Fort Worth Gold and Silver Exchange. Like a stock exchange. Only better, because anyone can buy. Anyone can walk off the street and get something for their money. It goes up in value! Popper, he's my boss, the owner, he gives stuff away. Every day in the paper. Twister beads, CZs, real gemstones. It's like he wants to help people. He's like a magic lamp! Wishes come true. That's what I am telling you. I am not trying to talk you into anything. You have to make your own mistakes."

Jim hung up. I called Wendy. I wanted to call her while I was enthusiastic. Wendy was the girlfriend.

"Why don't I come over?" I said. "What are you doing?"

"I have too much homework," she said. "I have chemistry homework and physics."

"That's bullshit homework. Do it before class starts. We'll do it together. I'll sneak into the library and help you with it. I'll meet you in the parking lot. I can do it there if you want. I can do it all for you. I know that stuff."

"I'm not learning it that way. We can't do it that way anymore. Anyway I have to get off the phone. I can't see you tonight. I am supposed to go to the grocery store with my mom."

"You are going to the grocery store?"

"I said I would. I said I would go with her."

"I could come over afterward."

I knew about the grocery store. There was a guy there. His name was Andrew. He was a basketball player. He went to a high school by Wendy's house. It was the high school she was supposed to go to before we met. Then she decided to go to my high school, which also had the honors program she wanted to be in, which was probably the honest reason she went there, and not falling in love with me. But whenever anything went wrong at Western it was on account of me that she had come to this lousy school. Now I was kicked out and she was hanging around the high school by her house. Now she even went to their basketball games. Now she was going to the grocery store with her mom because Andrew worked in the produce department. She imagined herself spinning on his cock in the iceberg lettuce bin. He might stick a cold cucumber up her ass. I remembered that when I was in third grade Sean DeBoer had said that to me: "You walk like you've got a cucumber stuck up your ass." I understood the remark.

Wendy was not a virgin but she preferred anal sex. She said it was because she could not take chances. As a matter of method she lied to herself first before lying to other people. Or she would lie with a truthful statement, like "I can't get pregnant if you come in my ass." That was true on its face but concealed her genuine agenda.

"Fine. I get it. Go see grocery boy. I'll just see you tomorrow."

"No, that's not what I'm saying. What I'm saying is maybe you shouldn't come over anymore."

"Is your mom mad at me?"

"I didn't want to say it. You made me. We shouldn't see each other anywhere. At all."

I listened to the telephone. I reassured myself. She did not understand the words that were coming from her mouth, and maybe did not even hear them.

"You're not even in high school anymore. I mean, what are you doing with yourself? What are you going to do? Just be a dropout? Sleep in the mall every day?"

To keep my mother in the dark in the morning when I was going to school I would just take the bus down to the zoo or to the mall. I did not really sleep there. Wendy said that because I had fallen asleep in the food court once and been kicked out by a security guard. I only started going to the mall because Wendy liked the Caesar salads from The Copper Creperie and I would bring them to her for lunch. I had to sneak in and out of my own high school. Because the principal, Mr. Robinson, had his eye out for me. He had chased me right down the main hallway and out the front doors only a few days before. I later told people that the reason I was expelled was that he had caught me in the hallway by one shoulder and I turned around and clocked him one, right in the nose, and he keeled over like a cut tree. Flat on his back, right there by the cafeteria doors. My old man had been a boxer and he had taught me how to throw a right cross and a few combinations.

"Maybe I should leave," I said. This is your chance, Clancy, I thought. Here is your advantage.

"Where are you going to go? When? Are you going to live with your brother? That's a good idea."

That was not the response I had expected. I did not even know how she might have known about that.

This is not love, I told myself. Someone who loves you should not talk like this.

"I thought you loved me," I said. That did not come out right either. "I mean, don't you love me?"

"I would only want you to go to Texas because I love you. Because you need a change. I wouldn't want you to go for any other reason."

"You want me to go? Because I will go if you really want me to go. But I don't think that's what you honestly want. I think if you ask yourself honestly you will know that's not what you want."

"What I'm saying is I know it's for your own good. Even

though I don't want you to go. You could go and then you could come back. That's what I'm saying."

"If you say you don't want me to go then I won't go."

I did not understand how it had happened that now I was going. Before this conversation had begun I knew I could never move down to Texas. What was I going to do, sell jewelry for a living?

"I think it's important that you go. That is what I am trying to say. I will miss you but sometimes it is good to miss a person. Then when you come back things will be different."

There was silence on my end. I wondered if she was in her bedroom, alone, or if she was in the kitchen with her mother listening. That would make a difference in what she was willing to admit.

"Is your mother there? Is your mother making you say that?"

Wendy's mother had liked me for the first several months. It was not difficult to arrange. I flattered her, dressed cleanly, and smiled often. "You have such nice teeth, Clancy," she often told me. "I just can't believe you never had braces." But then, a month or two before, she had found some pornographic letters I had written Wendy — it wasn't my idea, she insisted on them, it was a job I had to do in order to have regular sex with her — and her mother had found the letters, which in itself might not have been disastrous, but one of the letters was about a mother-daughter-boyfriend thing, and since then she could not tolerate me.

"No. I am in my bedroom. You need to go. It will be good for us," she said. She made that yawning noise she always made when she was lying.

"You are yawning," I said. "I know what that means."

"I am yawning because I am tired," she said.

"No, you are yawning because you really don't want me to go," I said. "You are yawning because you are lying when you say you want me to go."

She yawned again.

"You are right. I don't want you to go. But I think it's really important that you go."

"I'm going to go," I said. Now I had her right where I wanted her. Finally I had the advantage. I wanted her to ask me not to go. The threat of my going would make her abandon an infatuation with Andrew, I thought. If it has even gotten that far. She would realize how much she needed me if she thought I was truly going to leave. This is how women work, I thought. Just like the old saying.

"I'm going," I said.

"Good," she said. "I'm glad it's decided. I'm proud of you. But now I have to go. I have to go to the grocery store with my mother."

"What? You are doing what?"

"I slipped when I said that," she said. "I didn't mean to say that last part. I am staying home."

"Stay on the phone, then," I said.

"I have to go, Clancy. I have to do my homework. I am turning off my phone so I can do my homework. Otherwise you'll never hang up the phone. You'll just keep calling back and you won't let me work. I love you but I have to go now."

"I love you, too," I said. "I'm sorry," I said. But I knew she had hung up as soon as she told me she loved me. She always hung up before I could. That was how I preferred it.

4

"Your father's coming."

"What? Where?"

"Here. He's coming to Calgary. Tomorrow or the next day."

"From California?"

"It wasn't my idea. Your brother told him about your getting expelled from high school. He told him about Texas. I told him I won't even see him. I haven't told your stepfather yet. There's no reason to tell him. You won't say anything."

"Jim didn't tell Dad," I said. "Why did Dad have to know? Did you tell him, Mom?"

"It doesn't matter how your father knows. He is coming here and I couldn't talk him out of it. I think he'll be here tomorrow. He said you're not allowed to go into business with your brother. He said he doesn't want two con men for sons."

"He wouldn't say that. You are saying that. That's what you say."

"I didn't say anything. He said you're moving to Palm Springs with him. He said you can finish high school there."

"He said what?"

My father had never asked me to live with him before. He had often insisted that I could if I desired, but he had never requested it.

My mother scrubbed the dishes and thrust the clean plates and glasses roughly into the dishwasher.

"I did not think that is what he would say. I am not finishing high school, though. I am through with high school. I guess it wouldn't matter if it wasn't high school here."

"What's wrong with the high schools here? You can transfer to Central. You can transfer to Western where your brother went. Why do you hate it here so much? What have I done to make you hate it here?"

I feared she could begin to cry. Her eyes were suspiciously glassy, like she had been smoking pot. I would not tell her the truth because that would mean explaining about Wendy. She despised Wendy. If I told her Wendy had called my bluff so I had to move, she would know I was a liar.

But California offered an opportunity. I could avoid being a gemologist and yet keep my threat to Wendy. California would sound more glamorous to Wendy than Texas.

She would forget about me if I backed down now.

I had wanted to live with my father since I was ten years old.

"Are you sure he said I could live with him in California?" I knew better than to say that. My mother turned away from me, but slowly enough so that I could see her crying. She stood with her back to me at the kitchen sink and pretended to wash a dish.

"Why can't you two rinse off these dishes when you make nachos?" she said. I knew she wanted to say something so that I could hear her voice. "I ask you and ask you and you never do it. It is such a simple thing. This is how, exactly how, I lost my wedding ring. Cleaning up your messes. This is your fault, Clancy. Your father won't clean up after you like I do. You'll have to clean up your own messes, Clancy."

She did not cry often and it struck me. But I was glad she let me witness it. I knew how to rehabilitate myself when she thought she was being cunning with my love. That wasn't a motherly thing to do, I reminded her silently.

Then I understood she knew about the wedding ring. Because after the initial, suspicious search, it had not been mentioned until now.

"I am going downstairs." My bedroom was in the basement. "I am going to lift weights. So the music will be on."

I lay on my weight bench and did as many bench presses as I could. My father had been a weight lifter. He had won bronze and silver medals for the bench press, the clean and jerk, and the dead lift, in the Commonwealth Games. He was the one who wrote up this workout for me. But I didn't often follow his workout. It had too many leg and stomach exercises for me.

5

I was mowing the lawn when he arrived. This was unnecessary because it was September and the grass was discouraged by the coming Calgary winter, but I wanted my dad to see the joy it would be to have me with him everyday. "Bet you had not thought of that, old man." "He could be handy around the house." This way it looked like I had already mown the lawn because there was no new grass to mow, which also made the work easier.

He swung up in a white convertible rental car and there was a redhead with him. Wendy was a redhead, too. It is true what they say: they are more sexual than other women and often sexually deviant. He hopped out of the car without opening the door, like a man in a movie would or just like a happy, agile animal. The woman in the car laughed. But she did not get up. She inspected me curiously. She frowned at our house.

I turned off the lawn mower. But then it would not turn off. I did not know how to operate it. I turned the idle down as low as it would go.

He hugged me and I smelled the cinnamon pipe smoke and Gucci cologne in his beard. His arms were very tight around my ribs. I had grown since last Christmas and I was taller than he was, now. I enjoyed that and it made me nervous. He was weeping and laughing like he always did when he picked us up at the airport. "Boys, boys," he would say, hugging both of us, me and my little brother, Sean, or when we were younger, before my older brother lived with him, all three of us at once. Now he was saying, "Son, son."

"Turn that damn thing off," he said when he released me. He turned it off. "I can't hear myself think, Clancy. Why in God's name are you mowing the grass in September? This grass won't grow again until next June, for chrissake! You think you're in Florida? That's where we're going! South! Sunshine and oranges! Look at this piece of junk. Of course that cheap bastard your mother married would never buy a proper lawn mower. That thing must be as old as he is. What a dumb bunny. Typical."

"Florida?" I grinned happily. I blinked because my eyes were tearing up. I did not want him to see that. "I thought we were going to Palm Springs? Did you move back to Florida? Are we going to Palm Beach?"

"Here, come meet somebody," he said, and grabbed me by the shoulder like he did. Then he pulled me by the arm. "I want you to meet somebody. Meet your new stepmother," he said when he got me to the car.

"Billy!" she said.

I had never heard anyone call my father Billy before. Except himself, when he was telling a story from his parents' or his brother's point of view.

"This is my son."

"Jim?" she said.

"No, my middle son, Clancy," he said. "Clancy, say hi to Shirley. Clancy's the one I was telling you about. He's going to move down to California with me. Palm Springs. Smack dab in the middle of the desert. Never rains but it's green all year 'round. An oasis. It's a real-live oasis. You can come, too, Shirley. What do you, think, son? Should we invite her? Nice to have a woman around the old bachelor pad. Can you cook, Shirl? How's your French dip sandwich?"

"Bill!" she said. "He's only teasing," she said to me.

I was irritated by that remark. As though she would explain my father to me. "He's very handsome," she said to my father, and smiled at me. She seemed polite enough, I decided. At first I thought she was American, because she was sexy, but now I could see she was a Canadian woman. She did not look quite as good close-up. She still looked pretty good though.

"He gets that from his old man," he said. "The Martin genes! You should have seen his grandfather. Best-looking man in Winnipeg, Manitoba. He knew it, too," he said, and gave me a sly look. "The girls lined up for him! But he was a faithful husband. As far as one can be, that is. Within reason. He was a great man, your grandfather."

"Are you hungry, son? Want to go down to the Glencoe Club? Let's go show Shirley your old man's favorite haunt. You know what a Bill Martin cocktail is? We'll have them make you one, Shirley! Take two straws and stick them in a bottle of Bacardi. Slice of lime on the side. They call that a Billy Martin special down there. Get in the car, son! Let's go for a drive."

It was walking distance from the house, but I knew he would want to drive so that he could valet-park and go in the main entrance. I was not too excited to go because I had been fired from my job as a busboy there about a year before and had not been back since. (A mix-up about four vanished prime ribs. We had a bonfire at Stanley Park and pretended it was a luau, but with beef. The meat did not cook quite right but it was a warm July night and a good party.) I hoped they would probably be friendly enough once they saw I was with my father and his girlfriend. My dad did not know I had ever worked at the Glencoe Club. We had been members but after the divorce that was one of the first things to go. I did not mind. I hated the swimming lessons and badminton and tennis lessons. Although I had wanted to learn squash one day, and claimed for years afterward that I was an above-average squash player. I could not tell my dad that I had been a busboy there. He would be humiliated for both of us and angry at my mother. But I did not expect it would come up. Especially because I had been fired.

6

Wendy and I were suffering awkward sex on an oily blanket in the back of my borrowed tow truck. "It is your good-bye present," she said. "Your so-long fuck." I liked it when she talked that way but I did not like the expression "so-long." It was not intimate and did not reflect our true situation. "This is too much work," I told her after several minutes. "You are never going to come. Maybe if we move to the grass." I had my legs wrapped around the armature of the towing apparatus for leverage. "No, I am close, don't stop now," she said. "My mouth hurts," I said. "I'll make it worth your while. Don't stop. You're next," she said. "There. Right there," she said.

The tow truck came from another old job of mine, the Shell station on Sixth Street — down the street from the Safeway where Jim had first taught me to steal cigarettes, in fact, du Mauriers. My good friend Tim still worked at the Shell station, and because I got him the job, he would often allow me to borrow the tow truck for a few hours in the evening after Erik Jensen the redheaded Danish owner left.

"Wear my hat," Tim said. I hated to wear baseball hats but I put it on. "If you see him on the road, pull your hat down low. He'll think it's me on a tow. Give him a honk or something. Don't hide! But get the hell away from him."

"Calm down, Tim. He lives halfway to Lethbridge." Tim worried more than I did, and he later became a psychiatrist. "I know Erik. I know him better than you do. He's not in Calgary after five. He's a goddamn Mennonite or something. A Lutheran."

"I'm just saying. Just to be safe."

Erik did not like me anymore. Nevertheless, he had let me sleep in the garage for a week, one time, even after he had fired me.

"I think you cannot help yourself," he told me. That was a good way for him to think, I thought. But I was not sure he had convinced himself.

After Wendy came and the two or three minutes of my anal sex were over, we wiped up and rested on one another. That was frequently the only part of our sex that was thoroughly happy for me.

Wendy wanted to have sex for the pleasure of it. To me it seemed like a masculine quality in her. I did not trust it about her. I would not meet another woman like that for many years.

"How come you never brought this truck when you worked there?" she said.

"I didn't want to get fired," I said.

"But it's okay if Tim gets fired? Plus you got fired anyway. Those stupid coupon cards."

The coupon cards were a Shell promotion. They were scratch-off cards with gas amounts on them. I figured out the order of the cards they shipped to us and took all the good ones, all the ten and twenty dollar ones. It was because I sold them at a discount to my friends and other people we knew that Erik caught me. I told them not to come to my Shell station but they didn't listen.

"He wouldn't fire Tim for this. There's no way to get caught. Plus Tim could just say I stole it. I know where the keys are. I could sneak in and grab the keys while he was at the pump. That's what I would tell Erik Jensen. I wouldn't mind telling him that."

"I'm glad you brought it. Even if Tim does get fired. It was fun to do it back here. I wish you had brought a clean blanket, though. Can I have your jacket? It's getting cold out here."

Wendy lived in a new development on the north end of the city and we were parked out at the end of it in a field where new houses would eventually be. Beyond the field were pine trees. We could see the sun going down behind the mountains. All the mosquitoes were dead from the cold and it was nice to be in the field with the last bits of sun on the sparkly white tips of the mountains. I gave her my jacket. I was glad she asked for it. For the past few months she had not let me do things like that for her. We still had sex and talked the same way to one another, but in how she acted we were only friends. I was in a short-sleeved T-shirt and the hairs on my arms rose with the wind.

"It smells like it's going to snow," I said.

"I'm excited for you about your dad. I wasn't surprised but I was excited."

"I was surprised," I said. "I mean I would never tell him that, but still. You can come down, too. We can lay on the beach together."

"Do they have a beach in Palm Springs? I thought that was in the desert."

"We can drive to the beach. It's close. Plus we might be going back to Palm Beach. He says he misses Florida."

"Your dad has such a nice life," she said. "I wished I lived in California and Florida."

"I know. Me, too. I mean, I guess I will be."

She was quiet then and ran her hand across my stomach. I flinched because I did not want to have sex again. I knew that my flinching would upset her. But she did not notice and she continued to stroke my stomach. Then she put her hand under my T-shirt. Her hand was hot and gluey. Because my mother did not hold us growing up, I have never liked to be touched. I wanted to tell her to stop but it would destroy this happy few minutes so I kept my mouth shut.

"He used to live in this house right next to John Lennon," I said. "Once we were out on the balcony, Sean and I had a balcony right off of our bedroom, and I remember there were mirrors on the closet doors. We were out there and my dad was smoking his pipe and he pointed to the other balcony, the next house over, and he said, 'Do you boys know who the Beatles are?' I don't know where Jim was. I didn't know but I said that I did. Maybe I might have heard of them anyway. But I said yes and my dad said, 'That fellow over there is the one who started the band. That's John Lennon. He's a famous musician, boys. He's my next-door neighbor. Let that be a lesson to you, boys. You can be anything you want to be. He was just some poor kid in the streets of Liverpool and now he is famous and lives right next door to your old man.' He was playing a guitar and everything."

"That's a good story," Wendy said.

"It's true, too," I said. "I know it sounds made-up, but it's a true story. You can ask my dad."

"I'd like to meet him. You should invite me. You should invite me to dinner with him."

I knew Wendy was beautiful but I was not sure my dad would think so. He would think she was a bit thick in the ass.

"That is a good idea," I said. "He's pretty busy though. He has business to take care of while he's here. I will definitely ask him though."

She had her hand in my underwear now. She was patient and she knew what she was doing. She applied her intelligence very rigorously to sex, unlike most people.

"I'll give you a present if you ask him," she said. "I'll give you a present right there at dinner. We can sneak away."

"I'll ask him," I said. "I will sure try. He would like you," I said.

She laughed. "I am sure I will like him," she said.

I knew she would, of course. Every woman did. That was another reason not to invite her. Because of the comparison, I mean.

7

"Son, this is not the right time for you to move to the States. This an important time for you. Listen to what your mother is telling you. This is a time to finish high school and take care of your responsibilities. I don't like it any better than you do, son."

"Bill. That is not helpful."

"It's true, Vic. I am not going to lie to the boy."

I silently watched the betrayal develop. They were parents and so were expert at it. Even though they had been divorced for years, they fell easily back into the old pattern. Their deception was comfortable for me, too. I did not mind having them to blame.

The fact is you lie even more in families than you do with ordinary people.

We sat on the porch together. My stepfather was hiding in the house. Upstairs in their bedroom. We were talking on the porch because my father was not permitted in the house. My mother had brought out three chairs from the kitchen table. "I remember these chairs," my father said. "These used to be my chairs. I paid for these chairs. That's A.E. LePage money you're sitting on, Clancy. You remember when we picked these out, Vic?"

"It's just two more years, Clancy," my mother said. "Can't you stand living with me for two more years?"

"Don't do that to the boy, Vickie."

I remember that weekend I would sing the Beach Boys song "California Girls" to myself in my head. I wanted to sing it out loud for the two of them. I also thought of that John Denver song about Vietnam. "I'm leavin' on a jet plane / Don't know when I'll be back again." I stood up with the plan of taking a short walk. I tripped over my suitcase and stumbled down the stairs. I landed with my hands in the grass.

"You're being dramatic, son," my father said.

"He comes by that honestly," my mother said.

"Where do you think you are going, Clancy?" my father said. "We need to talk about this, son. You don't walk out on your mother like that."

"There's another one," my mother said. "You're full of them today, Bill."

"Nice, Vickie. Very nice."

They were standing now, too. I resisted the temptation to start off running. I was sixteen years old and I did not want it to look like I was running away from home.

8

The two airports were both slick with ice but otherwise wholly different. Back in Calgary the snow melted in the parking lot and Wendy stood at the curb. "Aren't you cold?" she said. I wore shorts and a T-shirt because I was going to Dallas. I had a backpack and a book she had given me to say good-bye. In the cover she had written, "Friends forever."

I tore the cover off once I was on the plane. I was angry and tearful. The old woman seated next to me inspected me with skepticism.

"Is this your first flight?" she asked me. "Are you afraid of flying? I don't want there to be any accidents."

"No," I said.

"Are you going to get sick?" she asked me. "Use the vomit bag if you are going to get sick. Maybe I should change seats. You look like someone who throws up on airplanes. I don't like that. I am an old woman."

From the windows in the airport we could see the runways and the fields beyond, and beyond them the dark line of the mountains.

The snow was more shiny than usual. I tried to take a good look around but I would not remember any of it. I had only hoped that Wendy would stop me so that I might turn around and come back. But she called my bluff. On the jet bridge I had paused. It was an honest moment with her. Those make me uncomfortable and unhappy. I turned, and as I turned, I saw the look of fear on her face. She was afraid that I would come back. She was grateful I was leaving. Or perhaps she thought she had made me leave and now that I was out of her hands I was suddenly free to change my mind. But I did not want to seem like a liar. If I left, I could show her that I had not invented the whole thing. About going to Texas and working for my brother and never coming back to Canada if it was true she loved Andrew more than me. She had not said that but it was implied by her actions, I told her.

On the other end, over Dallas-Fort Worth, we sat in a stack. I could see the other planes circling above and below us like some kid had pushed all of the buttons in an elevator. The captain explained that a freak ice storm that had struck Dallas and coated the runways and the wings of the aircraft on the ground. I knew it was my bad luck following us, as cold weather. Planes could not land or leave. The stewardesses distributed free drinks and I had a glass of champagne. The old woman sitting next to me was drunk. She complained when I unpacked the tinfoil my mother had wrapped two pieces of fried chicken in for my lunch. They served a meal on the plane but with the champagne I was hungry again.

"Are you really going to eat that?" she asked. There was an

odor to her enormous mouth. Her lipstick was smeared from drinking and it looked like a live animal might jump out of that red hole and bite me on the cheek. At last I vomited, twice, but missed her. She rose and tried to join another aisle but people were drunk and impatient. Then she fell and the stewardess insisted she return to her seat.

"I could have broken my leg," she told me. She pulled up her dress but I would not look at her white legs. "I have osteoporosis. My son is a doctor. This is your fault," she said. "If I get a bruise." She massaged her legs and I leaned my forehead on the plastic window so that I could not vomit again.

At last we landed. The Texans in the airport were bundled in overcoats, boots, and scarves, and they gaped at me in my shorts and backpack.

"Hell, that fella there thinks it's summertime."

"You been outside, boy? It's cold enough to knock a maggot off a gutwagon."

I saw Jim. I almost did not recognize him in his blue suit and red tie. The tie had pink rhinoceroses on it. Later I would see that Mr. Popper wore the same one.

"Come on, you are going to freeze," he said. "Here, take my coat."

We stepped outside and he lit a cigarette.

"You smoke now? No? That's good. But seriously you might want to take it up. It's productivity. It's been proven. You want to stay on your toes. Competition. They have the free market down here. Hey, here's the car, get in. Christ, these Texans. A little snow and they think it's the North Pole. We should set up a stand and sell fur coats. We'd be rich in an afternoon."

It was a white Cadillac limousine. I had never been in a limousine before.

"Sorry about the limo," he said. He grinned at me. His smile made me want to tell him about Wendy but I could not do that either.

"This is Lisa. Lisa, my little brother Clancy."

Seated in one of the white leather seats of the limousine, with her back to the driver so that Jim and I could sit together on the bench, was a woman.

"Hi, Clancy."

That was nice of her to use my name like that.

I did not know what to say to her. I tried to smile. But I was cold and shy.

"I tried to get a Rolls but apparently there's a convention in Dallas. Cosmetic surgeons. They sucked up all the best limos. I guess we better go shopping. I knew you wouldn't have the clothes for work but I didn't figure you'd show up in Bermuda shorts." He laughed. "I'm just kidding. I understand. Ready for a change. I've been there. You know that. But you can't walk into the store in that outfit. And we got to get back. It's slammed down there. Customers were standing half a mile around the block when I came into work this morning. With the ice storm and everything. People got the day off work, maybe. At seven o'clock in the morning. But it's one helluva sale. This Christmas is going to be something. I am really glad you're here. You're going to love it. Canada is the boondocks, don't kid yourself. You are in a real country now. Hey, have you ever tried this? You never have, have you. No time like today."

He showed me a small brown glass bottle about the size of half a thumb with a black plastic top like a doctor might use to inspect your eyes.

"Here, take a bump. Like this." He turned the bottle twice and inhaled sharply into each nostril. "It is pretty decent coke. Not bad. There you go. You'll like it. Go ahead, do a couple more. That's probably enough for a start. Oop, slow down. You gotta be careful with that stuff. Here, pass it over, I'll join you. Lisa? Your turn. I trade it with a fellow for help with his watches. He sells Rolexes in brown-town to all the small-timers. Crap mostly. Gold nugget bracelets, that kind of thing. He moves some merchandise though. There it is," he said. He rolled down the window. "Hot in here. That air will feel good on your skin. Cover your legs there. Here take my jacket and put it on your legs. See those towers? That's Dallas. Downtown Dallas. We are going to make a quick stop and pick up some watches from Granddad. He's a good old boy. You'll like him. He's a strange character. Half-dead from his liver. Keeps a submachine gun on the wall behind his desk. But he's the best secondhand Swiss watch dealer in the state. Then we'll go shopping and get you some clothes. Better shopping here in Dallas than in Fort Worth anyway. Get you some proper clothes, a suit, a pair of alligator shoes. We can still get back to work by three or four. I have a diamond appointment at four we can't miss. Here, pass me back that one-hitter. Okay. Your turn. A five-carat radiant. I've got it right here. Here take a look at this."

He opened his briefcase and took a small white paper from one of the pockets. He unfolded it. Inside the heavy white paper was a slender blue paper, like wax paper, and in the blue paper rested a diamond. It was the size of a nickel.

"Hold out your hand," he said. He picked it up with his fingers and dropped it in my palm.

"That's thirty thousand dollars you're holding. Thirty thousand dollars our cost. If I sell it today it's a five-thousand-dollar commission. Not bad, eh? One day's work, five grand."

"That's your brother," Lisa said. "It's not like that for everyone at the store."

I inspected the innocuous, glasslike stone. My palms were sweating and the water and oil coated the stone.

"Hey, give me back that bottle, would you? Go ahead and hit it one more time. No, get them both. Both nostrils. Pinch the other one as you do it."

He took the diamond from me, cleaned it with a blue cloth, and placed it back in his briefcase. "Then we better slow down. We've got a big day. This is your first day at work."

"He has to work today? Why don't you just show him the store today? He's fresh off the plane, Jim."

Jim handed her the bottle of cocaine and laughed.

"He's a Martin," he said. "He'll be fine. Won't you, Clancy? You want the day off? Hell you haven't even worked yet and you want a day off? I doubt it."

I did want the day off. But I knew I could not disappoint Jim. Especially not on my first day. In our family you are eager to work. But I did not want to seem ungrateful to Lisa. I was awkward.

"You're both working now?" I said. I directed the question to Jim but I looked aside at Lisa to see if she had heard me.

"Of course, we're working. Lisa here is my top saleswoman. She has a deal on a pink-gold Patek today. Patek Philippe. That's the best Swiss watch in the world. Best brand period. Skeleton back, moon face. You'll see when we get there. That's why she's coming to Granddad's. I wanted you guys to meet. You would have met anyway at the store but I wanted you to meet just the three of us."

He gave Lisa an odd look then that I did not understand. She smiled at him easily and looked out the window.

"It's snowing," she said. "I love the snow."

"Inside and outside!" Jim said, and laughed. I was embarrassed for him before Lisa about the joke. For years he embarrassed us both that way. Especially in foreign countries. "Hell, we may as well just finish this bottle. There's more where that came from. With a big deal like that it helps if you talk to the wholesaler. This old guy's in love with Lisa—"

"That's not true," she said.

"Of course, it's true," Jim said. "Like half the damn guys in the store. Myself included." He laughed.

"Don't listen to your brother," she said. "He's being ridiculous. He's joking with you."

"And you better not change his mind. Plus he's a real collector and this watch is a bargain so I figure he'll buy either way, but it still helps to hear the wholesaler describe the product. Granddad can show Lisa things about the watch that he could not explain over the phone. Plus she needs to see how he holds it, how he treats it. How he cares for it. This is not an ordinary watch. There's not much juice left in it. It's a thirty-thousand-dollar deal that we won't make three grand on. Hell, I'll show him the invoice. Of course we'll jew down Granddad a bit on the other end and pick up a grand or two. That's how you have to do it with these big collectors. They're practically in the business themselves. But you take care of them on these deals and the diamond studs at Christmas, the tennis necklace for the girlfriend, the steel Rolexes for his best employees, all the cherry stuff comes your way. Once you catch a crow you never let him go. Isn't that right, Lisa?"

"That's what he tells me," she said to me. "You're making your poor brother dizzy," she said to Jim.

She was correct: I was disoriented and my mouth was dry. For a minute longer I tried to seem lively. Then I gave up and rested my forehead against the cold, pleasant glass of the dark limousine window. I watched the long stripes of snow and the frozen highway outside. We were in the fast lane passing cars on our right. Everyone else was driving slowly and unsurely in the snow. Like they were walking and we were skiing past.

"Texans," Jim said. "You all right, buddy? Have another bump and then maybe take a little break. We'll stop for lunch after Granddad's and you can have a beer. That always helps me out when I'm a bit coked up. A beer is what you need. Still getting over the flight, I bet. He's always had a nervous stomach," he explained to Lisa. "Can't fly worth a damn, can't get on a boat. Can't even ride in the backseat of a car."

"I'm okay," I said. "Really I'm fine. I feel great."

"Close your eyes for a minute," Lisa said. "That's enough cocaine for right now. There's no hurry. You could put your head in my lap if you like." Did she say that or was I already asleep? I was not sleepy though. But with my eyes closed and my head lying back in the hot car it seemed as though I had disappeared.

"Close your eyes and we'll be there before you know it. Take off your tennis shoes." I was wide-awake. I did not want to take off my shoes because my socks were wet with sweat. I did not want Lisa to smell my feet. I am in the United States in a limousine with my head on the legs of a woman with black hair, I thought, and her fingernails on my eyebrows and ears.

"Close your eyes. We'll be there soon."

"You're spoiling him. Don't spoil him."

"Let him go to sleep. You don't have to torture him all the time. That's how my brothers always were."

"You had brothers? I didn't know you had brothers."

"Five of them. All older."

"That doesn't make sense. Still you are kind of boyish."

"It won't work. I am playing with Clancy right now."

I could not fall asleep but I pretended I was. I did not like to deceive her. But I wanted her to keep on talking that way.

My first job at Fort Worth Gold and Silver Exchange was setting the Swiss watches at ten to two. With automatics of course the movement is still unless the watch is moved, and winders you only wind every few months so that the oil does not settle and clog the movement. Therefore the hands on the watches in a showcase are motionless. Even with the quartz watches you withdraw the crown so that the watch will stop and the battery will last. It stimulates the customer when you give an automatic watch a twist before placing it on his wrist and it begins to run. Popping in the stem with a quartz has the same effect. They are set at ten to two because years ago Rolex began displaying their watches in photographs with the watches set at ten to two. If you try different hand positions on the watches, you will see they got it right. A watch looks best set at ten to two. Many years later a Rolex man in Zürich, Switzerland, told me that the V made by the hands is V for Victory. "But it does not work in German," he said, and laughed.

At the end of the day in any jewelry store many of the watches have been shown and so their hands have moved, which means that in the morning someone must reset them. Also the automatics may be stimulated into motion by being shuffled in and out of the cases, the trays they lie in, and the plastic tubs the trays lie in, when you put them in the safes and remove them again in the morning. My job was, after the watches were put out, to set them all at the right time.

I also vacuumed the floors, emptied the ashtrays and the garbage cans, and vacuumed Mr. Popper's steps.

"Son. Let me see that watch, there, son. That Big Daddy there. The gold one."

I was Windexing the Rolex case. It was Monday morning after the weekend Labor Day sale, so it was quiet on the showroom floor. I had done the trash, the ashtrays, and the vacuuming, but I was behind on the showcases because Jim had written one hundred and eighty thousand over the weekend so he slept in.

"We'll get there at nine," he had told me. When I woke him again fifteen minutes later, fearfully, he said, "Nine-thirty. Take the car if you want. Maybe I'll take the day off." I saw his coke next to the bed, and because I could hear his wife downstairs in the kitchen, I quickly did a line myself and then cut him a line and fed it to him. After a minute he sat up in bed and said, "Cut me another one of those, would you? Go ahead and have one yourself if you want." I cut us both two fat lines and he did one and said, "I'll save that one for after my shower." I did two more small lines while he was in the shower and tapped a couple of bumps into a piece of foil from his pack of cigarettes for later. Then we were in the car coming west on I-30 in the rush-hour traffic we normally missed because we drove in before dawn and there was downtown Fort Worth in the morning sun.

"Come on, son, get with the program! Ain't you had your coffee this morning? I want to see a watch! That gold one there. That there Rolex. The big one."

I didn't have case keys. I knew if I went to borrow a set of keys whoever I borrowed them from, even Jim, would ask me why I needed them, and then when I said there was a large black man in a black suit with three gold teeth and a white tie with a diamond tie stud at the Rolex case who wanted to look at a men's President I would be back to Windexing cases and someone else would be selling him. The reason I didn't have case keys was that I was not on the sales floor yet. They didn't even let me work the phones. But then I saw that the case was open. All of the cases were open. One of the last things you did before opening the doors in the morning was push all of the locks on the showcases. But this whole side, even the men's jewelry, all the way to the diamond room, stood open.

The men's President Rolex was displayed on the beige suede stand in the original walnut box all the men's Presidents were housed in. It had the silver plastic crown on its silver silk cord and the original green hanging tags. Underneath the suede stand I knew were the original warranty, books, and authenticity papers. I handled the heavy watch carefully. I almost dropped it as I slid it from its stand.

"This one, sir?" I asked, and handed him the watch. I did not know to unbuckle it before handing it to him, and I did not know that it was short links so that it would not close on his thick wrist.

He smiled at the watch. He slipped it onto his fingers. Then he turned it and looked at the back of the bracelet.

"What's the trick? How do you get it open?" he asked me.

"They call that an invisible buckle, sir," I said. "See that crown there? That little gold crown? Just flip that open with your finger."

He struggled with the bracelet of the watch for a moment

and then popped it open with his thumbnail. I took a quick look around the showroom but no one seemed to be paying us any attention. Four or five customers wandered the diamond jewelry counters. Larry was showing cluster rings to a fat woman with red hair, a tall man in a cowboy hat picked malachite, lapis lazuli, and rose quartz beads at the bead board, and one young woman with her two children stood patiently at the buy counter. Her baby cried from its stroller. There were only three salespeople on the floor and we had not even put out the brass numbers yet.

I looked back at my customer and he had the watch on his wrist. He was trying to close it but it wouldn't fit.

"I didn't figure they made these things so damn little."

"You have got a big wrist," I told him. "You're lucky. Look at it on me."

I took the watch from him — something I would never have done a year later — placed it on my own wrist and closed it. It hung there like a hoop. I shook the watch around my wrist.

"See that?" I said. "I would love to own one some day. But I could never wear one even if I could afford it. You need a man's wrist for one of these. My father always teases me about my wrists. He used to be a boxer. But he's got these same girlish wrists I've got." I took the watch off and handed it back to him. "It looks silly on me. I mean, it makes me look silly. It looks proper on you."

He slid the watch back on again. It almost fit his wrist with the buckle open. It would take five more links to fit him properly, I figured. I knew how to fit the links because I often installed them for Jim or for Dave when they were selling a President. You always started with fewer than you thought you needed. But this man's wrist was enormous.

"Well, what now, son? Are you gonna sell it to me or not? You gonna size it for me? How much you asking for this watch? This is the Presidential, right? This is the Rolex Presidential? This is the solid-gold watch, I'm guessing, correct?"

"Yes, sir. That's the men's President. Yes, sir, we will make it fit you. If you want it. I mean, the extra links come with the watch, if you buy it."

I didn't know to size it for him first, so that he could see it fit on his wrist. I also didn't know that the extra links were two hundred and fifty dollars apiece. That is, I knew we charged two hundred and fifty for men's Pres links. But I didn't know that we charged even when the customer was buying the watch.

"What did you say is the price on this watch? Is this the one I saw advertised in the paper?"

Today it is hard to believe, but at this time, in 1983, during the height of the eighties Texas oil boom, we were selling men's Presidents for four thousand nine hundred and ninety-five dollars. $4995.00. They were selling down the street at Haltom's — Fort Worth's registered Rolex dealer — for eleven thousand eight hundred. I did not know the details yet. I thought we were simply more honest and competitive. I thought we were just the best deal in town. That's what I told him, too.

"That's the one. Yes, sir. Forty-nine-ninety-five. A brand-new Rolex men's President, solid eighteen-karat gold, lifetime warranty."

"Hell, son, I think this one's broken. It just stopped. It just stopped ticking." He laughed. "You got another one in back? One that actually works? Or you going to make me a special deal on this one?" He handed me the watch. "I guess she needs a battery," he said.

I thought this was my closer. In fact, this could have been the most delicate moment in the transaction. I could have lost him here. But I didn't know any better.

"No, sir," I said. I gave the watch a little shake with that odd, back-and-forth movement of the wrist you use to restart an automatic, like the wave they teach a queen to use in a crowd. "That's the way it works. It doesn't take a battery. It works off the movement of your wrist. You never even have to wind it. They wind down from sitting in the case. That's one of my jobs, in fact," I said. "Every morning I come out here and get them all started. Must have been in a hurry this morning," I said and smiled. "I'm sorry about that, sir," I said.

"I won't tell if you don't," he said, and smiled back at me. "So your old man was a boxer," he said. "He must have had a few pounds on you," he said and laughed. "Well, you going to save me any money on this watch, son? What's the best price? You ask your boss what his best price is for cash money. If you can save me a little money, I think I'll take this one home."

I left the watch in his hands. I didn't do it because it was the right thing to do, though it was, but because I was afraid to ask for it back. I ran into the back of the house and went to the safe to find the link box, which was a clear plastic fishing tackle box with a white label on the side that said ROLEX that was kept full of men's and ladies' stainless-steel and stainless-and-gold jubilee and oyster links and eighteen-karat white and yellow gold links for the Presidents, and even some diamond pavé or bezel set links for the diamond Presidents, and pulled out five President links, made sure they were all the same size and all had screws, stole a screwdriver off of Roger's desk and hurried back onto the sales floor before a real salesperson would approach him and steal the sale. He was standing there admiring the watch on his wrist in a mirror that he had found. Next time bring the customer a mirror. Especially a black customer, I knew. The more you can serve them the better. Later I found out that this, too, was false. In fact, just the opposite is the case. But it takes years to learn how to sell. At this time I did not need to know how because I was innocent. You spend the rest of your career trying to recapture that. That is an advantage.

"What did the man say? You work him over for me? You give him the old one-two? The combination?"

I knew we had four thousand and fifty dollars in the men's Presidents we were running for forty-nine-ninety-five. These watches were almost loss leaders for us. To bring in the big fish.

"He said forty-seven hundred," I told him. I knew Jim and Dave would cut them down to forty-five-fifty, sometimes, to close a deal. "For cash."

"That's no sales tax, then," he said. "For cash. That's forty-seven tax, title and license. Out the door."

"Yes, sir. Forty-seven hundred out the door."

"Sold. You going to fix this so she fits me? I'll just wear her out. This thing come with a box? I can put my old Seiko in there. See what my wife thinks about that," he said, and laughed.

"Hell, that's not a bad way to start your Monday morning, is it, son? What did you say your name was?" He was counting hundred dollar bills onto the counter. My Windex bottle and my roll of paper towels were still sitting there on the corner. "Not everybody around here starts off the week with a five-thousand-dollar sale, I am willing to bet. Congratulations. I bet there's a fine commission for you on this. I sure hope so. You look awful young to be selling jewelry, come to think of it. You old enough to be out of high school? 'Course there ain't no shame in working for a living. I never finished high school myself. And look at me now. Buying a watch that is worn by presidents. That's how it got the name. Work hard and you'll be paying cash for one of these yourself some day, son."

"Yes, sir," I said. "I hope so, sir," I said. I finished installing the links and handed him the watch. I counted the money. There was forty-seven hundred dollars. I tucked it into the outside pocket of my jacket.

"Now I'm going to need an appraisal for this watch. For my insurance. Got to talk to my man Ken Monier later today. You can't wear a watch like this uninsured."

He shook the watch down to the end of his wrist, before the wrist joint. It fit. It was snug but it had just a bit of slide. You should be able to slip just the end of your pinkie finger between the bracelet and the base of the wrist.

"Put that box in a bag for me, would you, son? Stick that old

Seiko in there. Worn that watch for twenty years. My son will get it now. How's that look? Now that's a bit of sunshine. Look at that sparkle. That ain't half bad. See that? That looks like you made it."

"Yes, sir. That says success."

"Success? Hell, yes! That says, 'Look out! Here comes a rich man. A wealthy man. Mister Big Time!'" He laughed again. He had that large laugh of the older southern black man. "'Here comes a man who's got it all. That man has made it!' That ain't no flash watch. That there's the real deal. That is it. What will this appraise for? Eight, nine grand?"

"Eleven thousand eight hundred," I explained. "That's brand-new retail list price. If you had to walk in to Haltom's today and buy a new one out of their case that is what you would pay. So that's what we appraise them for. Retail replacement value."

"All right, well you get that in the mail to me tomorrow. It's been a pleasure. A real pleasure. You'll see me again. Yes, sir. You're my jeweler now. You got a card? Hell, you haven't even told me your name?"

"Clancy Martin, sir," I said. I shook his hand. I had not wanted to do that because my palms were wet with sweat. It was my first sale, plus the cocaine. "I'll put a card in the appraisal, sir." I did not have cards yet. But naturally I could not tell him that. After he left, I went along the line of watchcases and made sure all the cases were locked. I went into the diamond room and sat there for a minute in the red leather chair that was fashioned out of white and black bull's horns. I would have done a bump if it were not

59·

for the security camera. Besides newspapers on my paper route growing up, which didn't really count, and credit card applications I had sold at Sears for a few afternoons before they found out none of my applications were going through, that men's President was my first time, my first sale.

In the back of the house Jim was waiting for me. He was in the hallway next to the customers' bathroom, what we called the executive bathroom. It had real Frette hand towels and the expensive toilet paper. There was another bathroom in the back that we were all supposed to use. But the saleswomen only used this bathroom and it was the one I used, too, because if I had to, I could pretend I was only replacing the toilet paper or cleaning the mirror. I always had my Windex with me. It was a safer place to do a line, too.

This hallway was a small private space insulated from the rest of the store. The hallway led to the bookkeeper's room and then into the main part of the back of the house. The steps to Mr. Popper's office also led on to this hallway. Most of the salespeople went through the main doors into the back-of-the-house because it was quicker, and because you were less likely to run into Mr. Popper or his wife if you stayed out of this hallway. There was no real reason to be there so you were supposed to stay out of it, although there was no official rule. But I liked it because it was private and there were no cameras, and I often found Jim pausing there also. Like me he liked to use the executive bathroom. But he was probably allowed to, because he was the sales manager.

"Did you sell that watch? Did you sell that President? That was the display. You didn't sell the display, did you?"

I took the stack of hundred dollar bills from my pocket and handed it to him.

"I got forty-seven for it. Forty-seven is all right, right? He asked for a better price for cash. I didn't charge him sales tax."

"That was the display, Clancy. That was the last men's Pres in the store. We were taking orders off that watch. We don't have another one. We can only take orders on Presidents at that price. Did you write him a receipt? You have to charge sales tax if you write him a receipt."

"No, I didn't write him a receipt." The receipt was in my breast pocket. I had had it in my hand until he stopped me and I took out the money. I would still have been holding it if I hadn't needed both hands for the cash. I figured he did not have time to see it. I could just tear it up and flush it down the toilet.

"You didn't write him a receipt? Okay, that's good. Okay let's go tell Sheila you sold the floor model. At least you got cash. At least it's not a charge. She's going to shit. But it's okay, it's just Sheila. I'm not saying it wasn't a good sale. You didn't know. What were you doing out there? Why didn't you come get me? You did the right thing. You sold the watch. Nobody can say you didn't do the right thing. You made the sale. Good man. Hell, we shouldn't have the damn thing out there if it's not for sale. How could you know any better? It could have happened to anybody. Who would have guessed you would have sold the damn thing? You didn't even come to me for a price. You've got the instinct."

This was more or less the same pitch he gave Sheila in the bookkeeper's office. He was just rehearsing it for himself. She started to yell and then Jim showed her the cash and she settled down. That was why he told her the story before he showed her the money. Because he knew once she saw all that cash her volume would lower. Nevertheless, she explained to me how many different ways I had broken company policy and cost the store money. None of this made sense to me at the time. I came to see the wisdom of it later. By this time already, with Christmas still three and a half months away, we were not selling Rolexes at all, we were only selling Rolex orders. In fact, we never even intended to order any more Rolexes. Or maybe we intended to but never did.

In the middle of Sheila's speech Mr. Popper entered the office and she stopped.

"Did I hear right?" he asked. He had a small, barely curved grin on his face. He was wearing a red Hermès tie with pink elephants on it. "Did I hear what I think I heard? News around here is one of these Martin brothers sold himself a men's President first thing this morning. Now which one of you done it? Not this little one?" He patted me on the shoulder. Then he took two one-hundred-dollar bills off the pile of cash from my Rolex sale on the bookkeeper's desk and folded them in half and tucked them in the breast pocket of my jacket, in with the hidden receipt for the Rolex. "Hell, Sheila, sounds to me like we got another Martin here. Sounds like we might have found ourselves a salesman. Jim, why is this fella still stocking the box room? When were you planning on putting him on the floor? When he beats you on the boards? Looks like he's gonna sell whether you put him there or not!" He laughed again.

"You just listen to your big brother," he told me. "When you're ready, he'll let you sell. Sheila here is right. We got protocols for a reason. You just do like he does and you'll be all right. Hell, that's something, though. Doesn't even have a set of showcase keys and he's already sold his first President."

He knew before anyone else. His genius was an omniscience about the sales floor. He did not have the same understanding of the books and the back-of-the-house.

11

It was after hours, except for us the store was empty, and Jim had seven ladies' eighteen-karat gold Rolex bracelets lined up on his desk on two jewelry display pads. The bracelets were detached from their watch heads and, tapered at the buckle as they are, several of them bright with diamond center links. They looked like the elegant, slim-waisted and decapitated corpses of fashion models.

"We'll start with the ladies' President Oyster Rolex because that is the easiest with the fewest substitute parts."

"Substitute is counterfeit?"

"Say *substitute*. That way you don't slip when you are selling. *Counterfeit* confuses them. There is nothing wrong or illegal about replacing the parts on any product you own and then reselling it. You might tell a customer which parts have been replaced. But it is a case-by-case thing. Look him in the eye and assess the individual. Will they appreciate having new parts? The less you say the better. Let the customer buy the product he wants to buy. Never sell him the watch you want to sell him. There are enough diamonds in the basement vaults at De Beers to give a five-carat flawless to every man, woman, and child on the planet, Clancy. It's not like you're selling penicillin. There is no distinguishing between the real medicine and the placebo. No lives are in the balance. Like the fashion business or any luxury good. Your customer will be happy so long as you sell him what he is paying for. But if you try to sell him something else, he won't buy from you, he'll go down the street to Melman's and buy the same watch from some other, better salesman. You both get screwed. You lose the deal and he pays too much. And you have no one but yourself to blame." He paused. "You ready for another line?"

On the leather-top desk next to the two display pads was a Venetian glass mirror with a large gold Rolex crown embossed in its center, the crown approximately the size of a dinner plate, which Jim had taken off its stand and laid on its back, and on the mirror were four small, fat, toothpick-sized lines of cocaine. Like most career cocaine users Jim was good about cutting manageable lines. The mirror, he told me, was given to him by Dan Gardener, the Texas-Oklahoma-Arizona Rolex rep, when Jim sold his thirtieth brand-new mens' Pres. We were not registered Rolex dealers, but some customers could not be converted to a used or like-new or registered pre-owned Rolex and then Jim called Dan, and Dan sold the watch without the papers. Papers were not a problem for us, we had boxes and boxes of Rolex books and warranties and authenticity certificates in the big basement storage room. Mr. Popper had them printed in China by the same people who printed our Christmas catalog. New Yukon Love, they were called. You just filled in the serial number yourself.

"There is the ordinary world where you cut your finger and you drive your car to work. But you don't even live in that world," Jim said. "Think about how you walk down a hallway and you don't even know what the color of the walls is. You don't even know if it's paint or wallpaper. You don't even know what your own hands look like."

We each sniffed another line. It was excellent cocaine. Much better than I could ever buy from the Wizard downstairs.

"In your head is the world we work with. You doubt, perceive, affirm, deny, will, do not will, imagine also, and feel, and think. Get it? There's nothing real in that world," he said. "It's the world inside the mirror. That's what we are. People seeing themselves. Not what they see. How they see it. What doesn't matter at all. That is what I am showing you."

I wanted another line but instead I picked up a bracelet. The way it fell across your hand was like silk. It rolled over your knuckles.

"Take the band in your hand," Jim said. "Turn it over. See on the ladies' gold Rolex, first you look at the buckle. How we put them together there are four options. Here is a real Rolex bracelet. See how straight the stamping is on the buckle?"

We both louped the buckle on the underside of the bracelet.

"Same depth on all the letters and numbers. See that? Now

look at this Hong Kong bracelet, with the trapezoid crown. See how uneven the stamping is? And shallow on one end and deep on the other? That's not Swiss. Somebody underpaid and in a hurry. Of course, you know it is a replacement when you see that it is just a little triangle of gold for the flip clasp rather than a crown. They used to make them with crowns only, but Rolex blocked the shipment of these bracelets into the States and so they made them with this template, which is easy to use to solder on a crown you make yourself. See this one?"

He handed me another bracelet, one with a stripe of diamonds all the way up the center of the bracelet.

"This is almost entirely our own product. This is more Fort Worth Gold than Rolex USA. We started with a South American bracelet, because the color on these is better than on the Hong Kong bracelets — see how the Hong Kong bracelet is oranger than the Rolex bracelet? — and then used a Hong Kong buckle so that we could take a real crown off of an old, worn-out Rolex buckle and solder it on — loupe underneath that crown and you'll see the residue of the gold solder — and then had Time Stall over in Dallas drill out the center links for the bead-and-bright diamonds. Then I pulled the melee from a three-hundred-a-carat package — this is one of mine — and had Larry set it, and it looks just like a factory Rolex ladies' diamond center link. Now read the cost code, what does it say?"

We used the standard jeweler's cost code, which is to assign a number from 0 to 9 to each letter of a memorable name or phrase with eleven different letters, with the last letter standing for R or a repeat of the previous digit. Later, when we had our own store, we used "Martins Gold." 0-M, a-1, etc., and Repeat was d. Most of the sales force at Fort Worth Gold did not know the cost code. Because Jim was my older brother he let me in on this and many other valuable secrets.

"Twenty-five hundred," I said.

"Right! What do you think that bracelet would cost me if I ordered it from Dan? If it was a factory bracelet? Nine thousand dollars. Nine grand, our cost. Now tell me there isn't a lot of juice left in that when you sell it to a customer. Tell me how Melman's can compete with that?"

For three hours Jim quizzed me on the different styles of ladies' President bracelets: Brazilian, Italian, Hong Kong, factory Swiss; the buckles and the crowns; factory diamonds (Rolex uses single cuts and we use full round brilliant cuts, but you should only illustrate this for the customer if he already knows he is buying a watch with a replacement bracelet, in which case it is a virtue) versus Time Stall diamonds (better bead setting and nicer quality of individual stones, but expensive) and our own diamond links; and all of the possible combinations of hidden buckles, links, screws, and joining pieces. For us, Rolexes were an art, while a regular Rolex salesperson barely knew his own product. I was in the inner circle, however. Many of our own salespeople were not taught about the counterfeits.

"It doesn't help them sell if they have to worry about the different parts," he explained. "A salesperson should be clear in his mind. Blue-eyed lies. That is what you want. A frank expression.

The blue eyes of a clean conscience. That's something Ronnie taught me. Don't muddy your salesman's mind and he won't muddy the customer's."

A watch may have a factory Rolex head, though the serial number stamped on the outside of the case between the lugs has been altered to make the watch appear newer (you determine the age of the watch by the production date that corresponds to the serial number), that has a factory Rolex buckle though it comes from a different watch, whose band is made by an Italian company that can so closely duplicate the Rolex bracelet that they supply links to Rolex, whose face or dial was made by Rolex, and, in any event, any Rolex is available from the factory with almost any dial, whose hands, crystal, bezel, and crown all come from different off-market factories from different watch companies in different parts of the world — China, South America, Spain, and even Switzerland — and whose movement, finally, like the head, is once more made by Rolex, but was made for a different watch, quite possibly even a different model of watch (several different Rolex movements are the same size or close enough that they will fit snugly into several different styles of head), and has been serviced so many times that half the parts have been replaced, both by registered Rolex repairmen and ordinary watchmakers, both with factory and nonfactory parts. You give it a pressure test and a good external refinish, check the timing and wear it for a day to be sure it holds a wind, put it in a well-maintained used Rolex box (wholesale cost, forty bucks) or a new counterfeit Rolex box (wholesale, twenty-five) with papers and hanging tags and a better warranty than the registered Rolex dealer offers, and sell it as a like-new Rolex. And in fact to anything but a highly trained eye it looks exactly like the watch one would buy at a registered Rolex dealer but spend twice the money on. When your customer has it on his wrist and his buddies are admiring it on the golf course, what difference is there between his watch and the "real Rolex" his golfing partner bought down the street?

The problem was not restricted to Rolexes, their counterfeits, and the mix of old and new pieces of Rolexes—the complex combinations of factory and off-market parts went into almost every watch we sold. Take a diamond. There is of course a GIA certified diamond that actually matches the certificate and is the stone it claims to be. If it is a part of "The Kimberly Process" you can even know—or tell yourself that you know—the original provenance of the diamond, where it was mined, whether or not it was used to purchase machine guns, slaves, and machetes, if it was cut in India, Israel, Belgium, or Thailand, and how many hands it has passed through before it arrives in your retail store. But most diamonds do not have this title—and if you have been in the jewelry business for a few years, you know that Kimberly Process papers are more like a novel than a newspaper—and most diamonds are not certified by GIA but by one of a hundred different certifying agencies, most of whom are owned or controlled by the cutting houses or wholesalers who are selling the diamonds. Therefore, these diamonds are certified in a way that suits the seller of the stone. Further, like many jewelry stores around the world, we certified our own diamonds with a simplified version of the GIA system, "in order to clarify for the customer" the diamond-buying process. But if that layer of lies was not sufficient to obscure matters, many of the certified diamonds, from GIA all the way down to EGL and CGI and the worst of the labs that whore to wholesalers, were in fact not the diamonds originally certified, but merely stones that closely resembled the stones that originally had been weighed, measured, and evaluated for the official document. You could be selling a 2-carat E color VS1 round brilliant cut diamond to that rare, happy customer who is willing to pay for a GIA certified stone of this quality and in fact unbeknownst to both — you the unwitting liar, and your still more witless dupe — the stone is a 1.91 carat G SI2 that has been laser-drilled and the drill marks filled with a glassy substance that hides the fine lines and odd holes of the burns, and the papers are simply relaminated copies of the cert for some other diamond that the wholesaler or the wholesaler's supplier or your own boss or any past owner of the faked diamond you are selling still owns or sold long ago. Why should anyone care? He buys the diamond she wants for the price he is willing to pay. She gets the diamond she wants to show her mother and her girlfriends, a diamond he could never otherwise afford. The frustrating thing is that if you get caught, everyone blames the poor dumb jeweler. The jeweler was only trying to make all parties whole and happy.

"Oh, my God! It's magnificent! Can I ask?"

"Two carats."

"Two carats!"

"I know."

"Two carats? That Tom! He is so sweet! Mine is only one and a half, but we're upgrading next year. Dave promised."

"It's an E color, VS clarity. I don't really know what that means but Tom says it's supposed to be the best."

"Oh, that is the best. I went with Dave when we got ours and the jeweler explained the whole thing. He's our regular jeweler now. I guess the absolute best is A color and flawless but those practically don't exist. I mean, you can't ask for that."

"I don't think it goes to A color, does it? I think the highest is E? Or is it D?"

No one, not even you, the tired salesman selling the diamond, can tell the difference.

Falling in love with anything works the same way. It is still worse with colored stones. Years later as a consultant I went through the best houses in New York, Beverly Hills, and London — Cartier, Tiffany, Bulgari, the best — and picked at random various finished jewelry pieces with expensive color: sapphires, rubies, emeralds, tsavorite garnets, alexandrites, the best color the best jewelry stores in the world had to offer. We insisted we only wanted to see colored stones the jewelry stores knew were natural, untreated stones. We took them to the lab in New York. Not ten percent, not half, not ninety percent of the stones had been treated, enhanced in one way or another: irradiated, heated, drilled-and-filled, lab grown. One hundred percent. All of them. Every single stone. There was not a natural stone in the bunch. Which is not mysterious or even regrettable. It simply expands the definition of natural.

"They are all fakes," the gemologist said. "I don't believe it. I really can't believe it."

"Not fakes," I said. "At worst they are lies."

"It's very discouraging," he said.

"You're being silly," I said. I was irritated. "Why pretend you don't know your own business."

It's like Jim taught me that night. I once said to him that what I hated about lying is that it makes you lonely.

"That's why I don't lie to you," I said. "I don't like to feel like you don't know me." We were deep into the cocaine.

"No, no," he explained. "That's not right at all. You better learn how to lie, Clancy. "

PHOTOGRAPHS

BILL HAYWARD

These collaborative portraits — produced at more than thirty sites across the nation — begin with this understood provocation: Deliver yourself! All the words, marks, cut paper, and constructions are created by the subjects. Bill Hayward's *Unexpected Truths* (a forthcoming book and traveling exhibition) — inaugurated in 2002 — is a work in progress, producing historic markers for the twenty-first century. As of today, three hundred and fifty citizens are participants.

DON ELLIS

Cowboy

Livingston, Montana

TEQUILA MOCKINGBIRD

Art Curator/Singer/Writer/Actress

Los Angeles, California

VIVEK TIWARY

Writer/Director/Broadway Producer/Music Manager
New York, New York

JERRY IVERSON

Artist

Big Timber, Montana

LINDA IVERSON

Landscape Designer

Big Timber, Montana

MATT CUSICK

Painter

Brooklyn, New York

GALIENNE ERIKSEN

Singer

Brooklyn, New York

Dear Joe Diebes,

Chapelle

MIKE JONES

Denver, Colorado

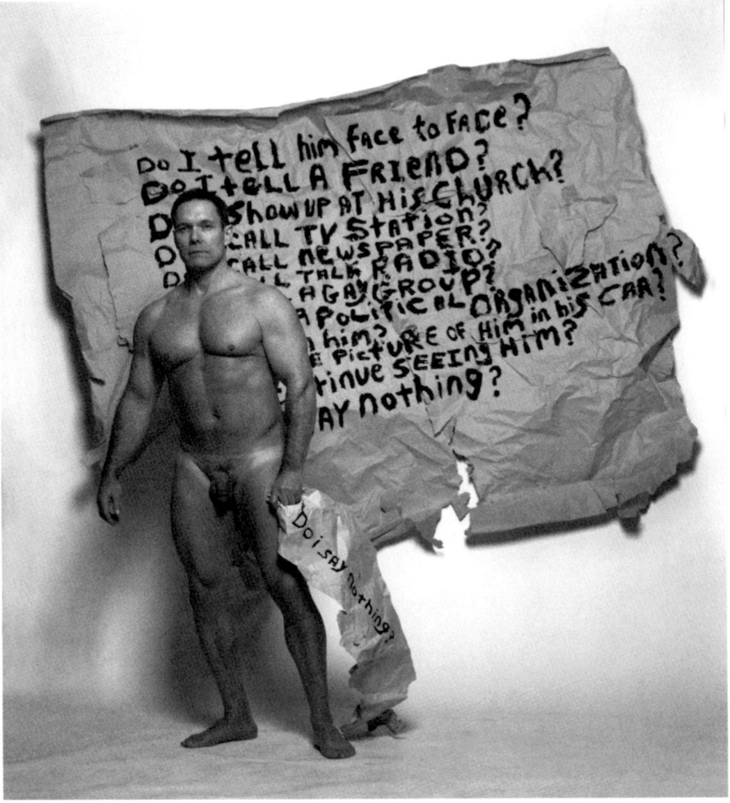
Do I tell him Face to FACE?
Do I tell A FRIEND?
Show UP AT His CHURCH?
CALL TV Station?
CALL NEWSPAPER?
CALL TALK RADIO?
A GAY GROUP?
POLITICAL ORGANIZATION?
PICTURE OF HIM in his CAR?
SEEING HIM?
nothing?
Do i say nothing?

WE HAD WONDERED WHAT ANIMAL MIGHT ARRIVE

LYDIA DAVIS

We had wondered what animal might arrive and then learned from another neighbor that the man across the street was acquiring Black Angus calves to fatten for his table. The calves were delivered early on Palm Sunday — from an upstairs window, we watched them run down the ramp of the livestock van — and soon after, the man's friends and family began to gather to take a look. They came by car, truck, and motorcycle, and stood by the fence or by the wooden gate, one foot up on a crossbar. The calves, bewildered, lowed and cantered here and there, side by side. Some of the men and boys walked inside the fence trying to approach them. A woman went around to the far side to take photographs.

We were having our own excitement by then. A skilled cabinetmaker who lives up the road from us had at last finished making a large bookcase for one of our rooms, after weeks of painstaking planning and building. It is made of local oak and runs the length of one entire wall. It is seven feet tall and trimmed with crown molding and flutes. The cabinetmaker wanted to bring his wife to see it. We said he should bring anyone he liked, and we would celebrate with a glass of wine, but he said it would be just his wife and she didn't drink wine, only soda.

But when he arrived that morning, as we saw out the window, there were more people with him. We went out and discovered not only his wife but his four grown daughters, all of them tall and slim with dark ponytails. One was accompanied by her boyfriend, and another had a baby in her arms. They were standing in the driveway and looking at the garden, and he explained that they were waiting for his mother-in-law, who, though she was blind in one eye, was coming in her own car. Just then she drove up and got out, saying "Here I am, One-eyed Jack!" We went inside and moved slowly, as a group, through the big old building, looking into every room. They were curious to see it, since it had once been a grammar school. It was built in 1930, among the first of the central schools that replaced the many one-room schoolhouses that we still see around here, some of them as small as a small bedroom.

When we were approaching the room, upstairs, where the bookcase was, we heard a voice calling from downstairs. A friend of one of the daughters had arrived late. Her father was with her, and she was carrying a very small puppy they had just adopted. With the puppy looking frightened and the baby content, the group at last arrived at the bookcase and were properly impressed. I took their picture standing in front of it.

About one month later, a third calf arrived. During the first week, it was nervous and broke out of the enclosure twice, once running up the road all the way past the Rural Cemetery. Then it settled down, and now the three cattle graze together. They are very quiet and do not low unless one happens to be shut in the barn and separated from the others. Two of them have strange white faces, like masks, but they rarely look up. They switch their tails constantly and vigorously from side to side as they graze, because of the flies. The other day, I realized they were growing up, because I saw two of them charging each other for the first time and butting their heads together. In another few months, perhaps, they will be large enough to slaughter for their meat. Then, I will miss their deep black against the green field, and their peaceful occupation.

COREY DAN ORMAND AND CHIQUITA JENNING

TAO LIN

I

"I've only had the opportunity to hold a hamster once," Chiquita Jenning said. "Its paws were so tiny. I think I cried a little."

Corey Dan Ormand said, "I saw a hamster eating its babies. I wanted to give it a high five. But it didn't know what a high five is."

"I would eat my babies if I had some," Chiquita Jenning said. "I don't have any babies."

Corey Dan Ormand said, "How old are you?"

2

About one month after they met on the Internet Corey Dan Ormand said on the Internet, "Can I come over and fry blueberries?"

Chiquita Jenning said, "Come over and fry things for two days straight."

"Two days of frying," Chiquita Jenning said.

"And rape you," Corey Dan Ormand said. "On the third day."

"Frying and raping," Chiquita Jenning said.

"Frying and raping," Corey Dan Ormand thought.

Corey Dan Ormand visited Chiquita Jenning in Pennsylvania about one week later. They walked around. They ate at a Chinese restaurant. They talked about what to do. They were afraid of Chiquita Jenning's mother.

At night they were near Chiquita Jenning's house and she walked into her house. Corey Dan Ormand stood on the street. The plan was that she would call his cell phone after she showered and her mother was inside her room. Then she would come outside and bring him in.

Corey Dan Ormand walked around a little on the street. He thought, Chiquita Jenning said she slept naked and her mother was afraid of seeing her naked so never opened her door at night. Corey Dan Ormand knew that Chiquita Jenning had been involved with an older person before and had run away to see him and that her mother had threatened to call the police and then the police had found Chiquita Jenning in Philadelphia and Chiquita Jenning's father had said, "I wish this would all just go away."

Corey Dan Ormand walked back and forth on the street and felt momentarily safe from terrible emotions. Walking, he thought, and looked at things. Waiting, he thought. A house had its door open very wide and inside was a yellow light and some people who were eating dinner. Corey Dan Ormand imagined either someone running into the house on an insane killing rampage or else someone running out of the house on an insane killing rampage. People were sitting in an SUV watching a movie. They seemed to be Latino. Corey Dan Ormand felt a little confused. He walked around and listened to music a little on his iPod. Here I am, he thought. Latino, he thought.

Chiquita Jenning called and came outside and saw Corey Dan Ormand.

4

He followed her inside the house upstairs into her room which was very dark.

She turned on a string of blue Christmas lights that were on one wall.

He looked at the walls. There were drawings and photos and posters that in a few months Chiquita Jenning would remove and put inside black garbage bags, to throw away. They sat on her bed. The bed was very low. She asked if he wanted music and he did and she put on music and he lay on the bed a little and covered his face with a blanket. He reached his arm out. He moved his arm around in the air.

5

Around 2:00 A.M. in Chiquita Jenning's room they faced one another under the covers with their lips touching but not kissing. Corey Dan Ormand stared at Chiquita Jenning's face and felt calm and alert. Their lips were touching for a long time and then she kissed him. Her lips were dry and he kissed her and licked her lips. The windows were up because Corey Dan Ormand was allergic to cat hairs. Chiquita Jenning usually did not put her windows up.

Chiquita Jenning's mother opened the door. "For God's sake, Chiquita Jenning," said Chiquita Jenning's mother.

Their heads were under the covers. Corey Dan Ormand scratched Chiquita Jenning's back a little with a finger that was already there.

"Put down those windows," Chiquita Jenning's mother said. "It's freezing in here."

"Put down those windows now," Chiquita Jenning's mother said.

"No, just let me have them up," Chiquita Jenning said. "Hearing the cars go by on the street helps me sleep."

"Clever," Corey Dan Ormand thought calmly. Corey Dan Ormand felt safe. Corey Dan Ormand felt a little clever.

"Just go away," Chiquita Jenning said. "Please."

Corey Dan Ormand heard Chiquita Jenning's mother say, "I can't reach that one," and then make some weak struggling noises.

Chiquita Jenning's mother left. Corey Dan Ormand moved farther away from the door to Chiquita Jenning's room until he was directly below the windows and off the bed a little. It was a very low-to-the-ground futon bed. Corey Dan Ormand said Chiquita Jenning's mother did not knock. Chiquita Jenning said her mother never knocked. Corey Dan Ormand said he was afraid.

"Come here," Chiquita Jenning said. She pulled Corey Dan Ormand and he moved closer to her, then stood and walked into Chiquita Jenning's closet and closed the door. Corey Dan Ormand still felt a little clever. Chiquita Jenning told him to come out. Corey Dan

Ormand came out and lay on her bed.

"You said she didn't come in at night," he said.

"She doesn't," Chiquita Jenning said. "It was because the window was up. The cold air got into the house."

"What if she comes back?"

"She won't," Chiquita Jenning said. "It was just the cold air from the window."

"Do you regret coming here?" Chiquita Jenning said. Corey Dan Ormand said he did not. Chiquita Jenning covered her face with her hands. Corey Dan Ormand pulled Chiquita Jenning's hands off Chiquita Jenning's face. Chiquita Jenning hugged Corey Dan Ormand very hard. They held each other on the bed. She twitched a little sometimes. Corey Dan Ormand wasn't sure if she was crying a little or dreaming. After a while he asked if she was asleep and she said a little and he woke her and he asked if she fell asleep and she said a little and he asked what time it was and she looked and said, "Shit." She went into the hallway and came back and said it was safe for him to go. She said to hurry. He left her house and ran into the middle of the street. He ran for about six minutes on a street, a sidewalk, a bridge, a field, and a concrete platform. He walked onto the train and sat on a seat.

6

A few days later Chiquita Jenning said lies to her mother in order to leave Pennsylvania to visit Corey Dan Ormand. On the train in Manhattan Chiquita Jenning and Corey Dan Ormand stood and held the pole. Corey Dan Ormand stared at parts of her face.

At Corey Dan Ormand's apartment they were kissing on the bed and they removed some clothing. Chiquita Jenning said it was okay. Chiquita Jenning said to do it. Corey Dan Ormand said something about a baby. "It's okay," Chiquita Jenning said.

They finished having sex.

Chiquita Jenning said it was okay.

In Union Square they saw a large baby sitting in a stroller. The baby looked about two or three. The baby was barking. "It's barking," Corey Dan Ormand said. They followed it a little.

They went to a restaurant called Congee Village. They ate porridge. They went back to Corey Dan Ormand's apartment. In the morning they took pictures of each other on the roof of Corey Dan Ormand's apartment building. They went to Penn Station and Chiquita Jenning went home on one of the trains.

The next day on the Internet Chiquita Jenning said she was drinking a giant glass of orange juice. "I need to stop," she said. "The baby is getting too many nutrients."

She said she would just starve herself. She talked about vitamin C.

"Hit your stomach," Corey Dan Ormand said.

"Babies are good," Chiquita Jenning said. "That baby barked."

"I want that baby."

"That was a good baby," Chiquita Jenning said. "It was lazy."

"It barked."

"It barks the parents into submission," Chiquita Jenning said.

"It knows how to use sound waves to confuse the parents' sense of balance," Corey Dan Ormand said. "At home it probably flies around like a bat and laughs at the parents."

"I want my baby to beat me into submission with a salmon," Chiquita Jenning said.

"I want my baby to drive a truck into my house over my bed when I'm sleeping," Corey Dan Ormand said.

7

The next Saturday in the morning Corey Dan Ormand wouldn't stand up. He was lying on the bed wearing boxer shorts. "Pull me," he said. Chiquita Jenning tried. She raped him a little with her hands. She said, "I'm going to rape you." She got on top of him and raped him.

Chiquita Jenning said, "You raped me like twenty times."

Corey Dan Ormand said, "Oh, yeah."

"Statutory," he said.

He knew someone who went to jail and they played poker every day and did ten minutes of work each day picking up cigarette stubs. The person was not ass-raped, cut with a knife, or beaten. Corey Dan Ormand would go to jail if he had to and be calm about it. He didn't want to go to jail, but he didn't want to do a lot of things.

CHUCK, WHAT IS THAT?

LAURENCE C. PEACOCK

"Chuck, what is that up in that tree?" Marie said.

Chuck walked to the window. "A man," he answered.

"A man? What's he doing up there?"

"Don't know."

Marie remained silent, before she said, "Maybe you ought to check."

Chuck put on his shoes, then examined the tree again. "That's Jim," he said.

"Our next-door Jim?" Marie said.

Chuck turned back toward his wife as he reached the front door. "I didn't think Jim's wife looked that bad."

"Don't be stupid," Marie said. "Maybe, a bear chased him up there."

"Bears climb trees, you know," Chuck replied. "Anyway, there are no bears around here."

Surveying all around his neighbor's lawn, Chuck slowly approached the tree.

He said, hesitatingly, "Hi, Jim."

"Hi," Jim said, as if everything were normal.

"What are you doing up there?" Chuck asked.

"Is something wrong?" Jim replied. "It's my tree, in my own lawn."

"Uh, yes, Jim. It certainly is your tree. . . . I understand. Have a good day."

Jim said nothing, and Chuck, while making his way back to his front porch, searched for any obvious reason for his neighbor's actions. He found none.

Marie held the door open for her husband. "What did he say?" she said.

"He says it's his tree."

Marie stared at Chuck. "I don't understand," she said.

"That makes two of us," Chuck said. "Perhaps, you should call Angie. We know Jim doesn't drink."

Marie picked up the phone, then placed it back in its cradle. "What am I supposed to say? 'Did you know your husband is up in a tree?'"

Chuck appeared to be a little uncertain. "Maybe, you could just ask if everything is all right."

Marie walked back to the window. "He's still up there. This is absurd. I am going to call Angie." She spoke into the phone,

"Good morning, Angie. Is everything all right this morning? . . . Yes, we are fine."

Marie covered the mouthpiece, and whispered, "She says everything is fine."

Chuck moved closer to his wife so he wouldn't miss anything.

"I assume Jim is going strong this morning," Marie added.

Chuck cupped his hand at his ear in anticipation of an explanation.

Marie hung up the phone. She said, "Angie said that Jim is fine. He is up in his tree."

SIMULATION

KIM CHINQUEE

A man doctored me up, cutting open my pant leg, making up an ugly wound with clay and food color. He put a tag on me, tying it to my boot, dumped me in the bushes. Now I was an airman and this was my role. Another man came and read my tag, picked me up, and put me on his shoulders. He was a reservist. I could feel his boot hit the ground, like a horse. Someone yelled and the man got down and dumped me. He fell on me. Said we had to stay there. I felt like a kid again.

MOO

KIM CHINQUEE

My grandma butchered chickens, and they were everywhere, not just in the freezer, but on shelves. There was even a room just for the potatoes, where she'd go down and pick a pail full, then go back up, peeling them, then boiling. She'd send someone to the barn to get milk from the tank. But you can learn a lot from watching, and now the aunts and uncles stayed upstairs, playing games like Smear and Sheepshead, and the kids, we drank our pop. We bounced around. We'd play. My grandfather was the cook. The adults sat and ate at their card tables, as if the games were still on. There had been a party! At first, when I was younger, watching my aunts and uncles, I always wondered what they were doing. My grandfather would get out his mechanical cow. It was clean and always looked new, unlike so many things there: worn tiles of the kitchen floor, the barnyard smell, the crumbs and dirty dishes on the counter. He'd go to his file cabinet and remove the box and set it down, getting out the cow and standing her. Then he'd press a button on his small remote with his middle finger, since he had no index, and the children would sit on the floor, anticipating, watching. He'd press one button, and the cow walked, swaying, unlike the real cows yards away. Then, with another movement, the cow would stop and raise her head, and she'd moo. It was a long moo.

COEUR

DAWN RAFFEL

He needs her to look into the pumpkin's face.

"Mind yourself—" her mother's voice inside of her, serrated and worn. She should clean up the mess.

"*Madre*," he says. "*Mama mia. Maman*!"

The eye he has cut is a heart she sees, if a heart were heart-shaped. "How do you say it in French?" he says.

She fires the oven.

"Salt," she says.

"You aren't even listening. Mother," he says.

"Buddy," she says, either scolding or pleading: can't keep her hands off, not for long, and never could. "Hands to yourself" — it is the story of her life.

Once upon a time, there was a girl with an empty place in her glove, an actual person known to Faye or, at least, described to her, minus the details. There but for the grace of God.

A slip of the knife has ruined the mouth.

All of the faces she has known, has loved, has watched fall!

All along the walls, there are the marks of the boy, in pencil and in fingerprint. In crayon and Cray-Pas, wax, sweat, on paper and not, in pulp, in ink, in shadow, scratched.

The oven clicks.

She is squatting to his level. "Here is the way that you say it," she says.

"Hold still," she says. "Don't move." She is tying a knot, or trying to. He holds a sword.

"Dagger," he tells her, by way of correction. Rubberized and bendable.

"I cannot allow," she says.

"I simply forbid," she says.

"You cannot walk alone," she says. "The river, and who-knows-who about. You know what could happen."

"How do you know?"

"Not going to say it again," she says. There is a hand in a pocket searching for something, a residue she feels against her teeth. "Not going to say it. Unpleasant," she says.

He is pulling the costume off himself, up over his head, the ends undone. Up, up in arms. Silvered legs are on the floor. She picks up the garment. The weapon has fallen. "Buddy," she says.

"Don't call me that."

"*Senor*," she says. "*Monsieur?*"

"Hello?" she says. "I'm hanging up."

She is holding a jacket, an empty sleeve. "I could tell you a story," she says, and does not. She is the keeper of mishaps: flukish and apocryphal, occasionally true. She holds it close: the story in the news about the woman who drowned, a woman who stole things, reckless and possibly somewhat distractible or, Faye thought, aloof. She had a beautiful name. She had a lopsided sidestroke, a light plait of hair. She had appeared, Faye thought, to be engaged, in a hurry, as Faye is herself, as if to finish up or polish something off.

She says, "I haven't got all night."

She says, "Speed it along."

She says, "Here is a flashlight. Other hand."

She says, "At least." She is always, she is thinking, doing most of the talking.

"What 'at least?'"

"At least," she says. She rights a strap. "At least it's not raining. Not too cold. Look," she says, for here they are, walking, persuaded into costume — the boy is <u>at least</u> — and out of the house. "Ghost," she says. "Look, look, a little goblin! Lower the beam."

He does as he's told, illuminates a foot, the curb, a leafy menace.

The child of the woman who drowned is in the walkway, surrounded by men. She is dressed as a fairy under her coat, as best Faye can tell. She is wearing a tiara.

Buddy says no. "Halo," he says.

"Where is a match?" Faye says to him or to else herself. "At least it's nice and warm in here." Disorder of the day: the newspaper spoiled with vegetable matter, marker, salt.

"Why did we walk away?" he says.

"Look up there" — there is a shelfful of things that are presumably dangerous and easy to reach.

She has the phone off the cradle.

"Mom," he says.

"Who is there?"

"Why?" he says.

She says, "I won't repeat myself," into the receiver. "Tell me what you want," she says. "This must cease. Buddy," she says, "please give me that."

"Why not just hang up?" he says.

"I am," she says.

Flint. He is lighting the candle inside of the pumpkin, precariously balanced. Flesh is burnt inside the thing.

Faye has heard the breathing. She opens her mouth to feed herself handfuls. "Want some?" she says.

"You need to drip the wax," she says.

"Careful," she says.

"Let me," she says, and knows he won't.

"Seeds?" she says.

"I thought you were hanging up," he says.

"I did," she says, depressing a button. "Buddy, listen, at least you have me."

"Curr?" he says.

"*Coeur*," she says. "The way that you say it," tucking him in. She knows it won't last. He'll be up in a minute. "A cur is a dog."

"It is?" he says.

"Yes," she says. "A mean one at that."

He proves her right.

"Can't sleep," he says.

"I know," she says. "Your father also never slept."

"My dad?" he says.

She ought to do something maternal, she knows. Tell him a story. "My mother would tell me a story," she says. "I just can't think."

"You said 'my dad.'"

"I did," she says.

"Tell me something else," he says.

"Like what?" she says.

"Something."

There is a crack in the glass in the morning; Faye sees it. "Look at the window," she says. "It's shot."

"Shot?" he says.

"Cracked," she says.

"How did it happen? Was it a bad guy?"

"No," she says. "I doubt it."

"I'll cut him," he says.

"It wasn't a bad guy."

"Who?" he says. "Who did it, then?"

"For certain," she says, "it was only the weather, or maybe a prank, or else the pane was unstable."

"Or maybe," the boy says, "it might have been a cur."

The boy knows better. Of course he does. He will not rest. "*Maman*," he says. "You promised a story."

"Once upon a time," she says, "there once was a mother who loved her little boy. . . ."

"Mom," he says. "A story. A real one."

"Stop it," he says.

"Get off me," he says.

"I can't," she says.

"Mom!"

"On the night you were born, there was a fire in the hospital."

"Really?" he says.

"Really," she says.

"Cool," he says.

"They sounded the alarm. Everyone evacuated, even the babies."

"Me?" he says.

"You," she says. "At least it was nice out. I thought it was a sign," she says.

"Of what?" he says.

"I really couldn't tell you."

"What happened?" he says.

"The fire," he says.

It had to mean something, is what she had thought. "What else?" she says. "They put it out."

THE PLACE OF NO PLACE IN DAWN
RAFFEL'S *CARRYING THE BODY*

MONICA MANOLESCU-OANCEA
Translated from the French by Monica Manolescu-Oancea

LANDMARKS: "WHERE ARE YOU?"

The first step into the interrogative domain opened up by *Carrying the Body* leads one to question the nature of the book itself. The book's cover copy informs the reader from the outset that *Carrying the Body* is "a novel." However, the presence and role of the narrative line are highly ambiguous, if not downright obscure. Since *Carrying the Body* professes to belong to the novel genre,

---

This essay originally appeared in French in the publication of a special issue (#38, June 2005) of *Les Cahiers Charles V*: "États-Unis: formes récentes de l'imagination littéraire (II: 'Recent American Letters')," resulting from the research work conducted at the Observatoire de Littérature Américaine (Paris 7-Denis Diderot) under the direction of Marc Chenétier, Professor of American Literature, Institut Universitaire de France, editor of this collection of essays.

one expects and occasionally senses there is a narrative line that insidiously hides and coils here and there in the text. Is this a book "about" something? This "aboutness" is certainly suggested as a mirage or a lure. The reader is promised a sequence of events, action unfolding if not in a neat traditional chronology, at least in a tortuous, but retrievable one.

Should the reader persist in looking for meaning and plot in a traditional approach or should the reader accept that these are absent and focus rather on the autotelic world of linguistic construction? As far as the narrative line is concerned, the reader's encounter with the novel is mediated by the comments on the back cover, which tame and thereby disfigure the fractured ambiguity of the text, neatly and falsely conferring on it narrative coherence:

> Elise, a young woman with a mysteriously ill son, returns to her childhood home years after running away with a lover. Now destitute, she begins to search for an object hidden somewhere in the house, which has been in a state of disrepair since her mother's untimely death. Her father, who fled political terror in his youth, is frail and often dreaming. So it falls to Elise's older sister, who has never left home, to maintain family order. Unraveled by alcohol and her own longing for escape, "Aunt," as Elise's sister is simply known, is further disturbed by the child's illness and his mother's irresponsibility.[1]

---

1. Dawn Raffel, *Carrying the Body* (New York: Scribner, 2002). All references to this edition are given parenthetically in the text.

The first-time reader might succumb to this illusion of wholeness and clarity, but once the reading adventure has begun, the quoted summary seems to encapsulate a different book altogether. The skillful abstract certainly responds to (and panders to) a primitive longing for narrative order, but the text itself resists such an approach precisely because it dangles between plot and accumulation of linguistic strata, character construction and pure linguistic play. The author's comments, in a 2002 interview with Dina Di Maio, tend to indulge the reader's desire for meaning: "I wanted to go into as dark and scary a place as I could and come out plausibly on the side of light. And I wanted to look at our universal failure to love completely and perfectly, and to look at how we might redeem ourselves."[2] The novel thus becomes a fable about solitude in the modern world, based upon a scenario of fall and redemption. The theme is certainly familiar, part of an archetypal parable. Mutatis mutandis, one cannot help thinking of Gabriel García Márquez's *One Hundred Years of Solitude*, a novel of isolation and lovelessness telling the story of the rise and fall of a world that is eventually saved by redeeming passion.

Carrying the Body is composed of a multitude of brief chapters bearing short titles ("Squeal," "Gin") which are sometimes replaced by unexpected poetic formulations, reminiscent of the lyrical titles of haikus and of Asian etchings: "Father, in a Rare Lucid Hour, Speaks," "A Particular Flower with Astringent Qualities, Often Used in Winter Bouquets." The division into chapters

---

2. Dawn Raffel interviewed by Dina Di Maio (2002), http://www.thesquaretable. com/winter03/dawn.htm

is mirrored by the image of the house at the novel's center, an architectural entity divided into various rooms. The reader is continuously dragged through the dark, dilapidated house, generally at night, through the heat of an endless summer, and thus becomes the companion of the elliptical narrative voice of the text, a voice belonging to a character devoid of an autonomous identity, possessing only a relational, oblique identity. Mimicking Dunyazad, Scheherazade's sister, the central character of *Carrying the Body* is "her sister's sister," a family appendix defined exclusively through references to other family members. She is also referred to as "the aunt" or "the father's daughter," with the help of a certain number of convoluted, substitutive labels that totally obliterate her real name, if any, and that consolidate her ancillary status within a spidery web of family relations. The aunt is an immobile being who seems to have always been cloistered inside the house, hopelessly caught in a petrified flux of putrefied matter, among decorative objects of bygone days invariably cluttering the rooms. Nothing seems to have survived of *The Fall of the House of Usher* and of the archetypal house of American literature: the resonant Gothic vaults, cracked, but majestic, have been supplanted by an endless leak of organic matter, by foul decay that contrasts sharply with the chipped china having belonged to a dead mother. Residual traces of the archetypal Gothic are nevertheless still present in an almost tangible blend of mystery and anxiety exuded by the shadowed corners of the house, seeping into the recurrent interrogations of the text, generally left unanswered. A nameless evil gnaws humans and objects alike, both cursed with the shrunken appearance of old age, with degenerative disease, with idiotic muteness or incoherent ravings: "The chair in an unbudgeable condition of recline" (6), "The breath of the child smelled to her of disease" (111).

Edgar Allan Poe's House of Usher is maybe less relevant an example than Miss Havisham's Satis House in Charles Dickens's *Great Expectations*. Dawn Raffel similarly presents a profusion of objects that have survived existential shipwrecks, shriveled bodies moving perfunctorily in a patchy, rotten setting, with the effect of an obvious mirroring of human and material corruption. *Carrying the Body* speaks of tainted substances and textures, of the weight of bodies and the ruin of architecture in the context of a generalized decline and decadence. An analogy is drawn between the house and the body, based not on the idea of volume, but rather on the idea of decrepit substance that constitutes both. The sumptuous nineteenth-century Gothic has been supplanted by a domestic Gothic of insidious, proliferating trinkets akin to rubbish, which fill the house and the page with their faded glory. The old bride is enthroned in the middle of the ruins in the shape of a china doll (20)—the splendid trace of a graceful past. The title of the first section of the book, "The Bride," seems to endorse the Dickensian reference, which is also supported by the presence of a young boy, the aunt's nephew, James or Jim, reminiscent of Pip.

No global view of the house is offered. It is replaced by a sequence of microtexts that cut up both space and narrative. The interrogation that opens the book is highly relevant for the reader's desire to situate the characters and the plot, as he or she faces the unstoppable invasion of chaos: "Where are you? he said" (the epigraph is taken from *Gen.* 3:9). This postlapsarian question uttered by God marks the isolation of Adam and Eve in paradise, where they try to hide from the divine eye. Similarly, the characters hide away from the reader's inquisitive eye, prompting basic questions like *who, when, where, what, why?* The title of the first section, "Late," is highly eloquent: while it appears to answer the question "When does the action take place?" or "What is the time frame?" and thus situate the chronology of the diegesis, it simply indicates that it is late. Thus, specific chronological details are replaced by a vague indication of a relational temporality, of belatedness conveyed by a floating, dreamy "late" cut off from any previous moment that could have more clearly defined it. The reader, having soon realized there is no definite narrative direction to follow, learns to ramble aimlessly with the text (and in the text) and to enjoy the rambling rather than try to find the North Pole. Fundamental categories related to the novel (character, plot, setting) are radically dismantled or blurred. This process reminds one of John Hawkes's dismemberment of traditional fictional categories in *The Cannibal* (1949):

> I began to write fiction on the assumption that the true enemies of the novel were plot, character, setting and theme, and having once abandoned these familiar ways of thinking about fiction, totality of fiction or structure was really all that remained. And structure — verbal and psychological coherence — is still my largest concern as a writer.[3]

---

3. "John Hawkes: An Interview," *Wisconsin Studies in Contemporary Literature* 6, no. 2 (1965):145.

Placed within this tradition of literary disruption, *Carrying the Body* emerges as an a-narrative narrative, a text that preserves the illusion of narrative while at the same time seriously undermining it from beginning to end. Nothing or almost nothing happens, except for a stifling repetition of gestures and actions: the lonely walks of the aunt inside the house, in the opacity of the night, the sighs and coughs of the father sprawled in his chair (a living corpse or a grotesque doll), the recurrent sleep of the child, haunted by unspeakable fears, the stories that the aunt strives to tell her nephew starting with *Three Little Pigs*. The human body, verging on the inanimate, is carefully staged, in its perceptible or infinitesimal moves within the house. Nathalie Sarraute's *Tropismes* (1939) is a kindred text from the point of view of its emphasis on bodily movement and on the inner vibrations of the body slowly progressing within a confined space. With its tortured claustrophobic characters, its philosophy of the minute movements, of the subtle metamorphoses that are at the origin of human actions and gestures, *Tropismes* appears as the modernist precursor of Dawn Raffel's novel.

In *Carrying the Body* there is no causality, origin or explanation for present actions, whose motivations are obliterated by pathologic repetition. The reader scratches the surface of phenomena, the outer crust of events, gliding on an epidermic narrative of surfaces. Instead of answers, we are faced with unanswerable questions: why has the sister, Elise, come back to the house after her adolescent elopement with a sibylline man? Why does she disappear again, mysteriously, leaving her son behind at the house, with her unsound relatives? What is she looking for among the antique, apparently valueless objects that fill the house? The past, where one is tempted to look for the source of present evil, is scattered in insufficient fragments. When looking in that direction, one finds a starchy mother obsessed with noble manners, fiercely intent on transforming her daughters into models of behavior conforming to the stiff ideal of decorum and decency. This maternal figure invariably accompanied by floral smells represents the only past memory the characters seem to possess: the image of the mother creates a breach in the bleak present and offers the only proof of the existence of personal memory. The characters' memories are otherwise empty, and the past simply does not exist, being repressed or invisible. The mother is a spot of color in the blackness of the novel, a person who diligently collected jewelry, delicate gloves, mother-of-pearl purses, china lamps, a wardrobe full of elegant clothes now eaten by moths, venerable vestiges of a vainly refined past, still admired by the two daughters. The mother looms large above the useless quests of the characters and gives them a semblance of psychological perspective. The wasteland of the house thus becomes a melancholic assemblage of relics. However, no explanation emerges from the shadows: the colorful heaps of old clothes and dusty gloves do not offer any enlightening clue about the meaning of present actions.

While many questions go unanswered, economically and laconically treated, the text offers a wealth of details on the privileged subject of family relations. The family is reconstituted and named starting from a series of core elements or nominal units (*father, child, sister*): "The father of the aunt and the mother of the child did not answer" (21). One cannot find in *Carrying the Body* lengthy talkative passages, and the general impression is that of an extreme economy of speech, a phenomenon that is explicitly mentioned in one of the versions of *Three Little Pigs* that the aunt narrates to the child. The following statement appears to possess the status of a genuine manifesto: "The father pig, whose story, for reasons of history, remains untold, was given, quite likely, the aunt said, to certain tenacious economies of speech" (91). However, this miserly restraint is accompanied by the reverse phenomenon of constant repetition: speech verbs and nouns designating family relations are endlessly repeated. There is an abundance of "he said/she said," except when the father's answers are introduced, since he does not "say" anything, in the proper sense of the word, but rather mumbles or grumbles, seldom resorting to the luxury of articulated speech: "Father? the aunt said. Something refreshing? The father (the aunt could have surely attested) grunted. The aunt smelled something heavily floral. Sweet? Said the father. Sweet? Sweet? No, said the aunt. Not her, said the aunt. I am sorry to say it, Mother is dead" (24). Dawn Raffel's style is brittle, disjointed, ruptured. Sentences are often interrupted by commas and dashes, characterized by a backward movement that stems the flow of syntax: "The room — hers — once hers, unassembled by night — still night, too damp, her nightdress damp — appeared most lightless" (46).

The same repetition of speech verbs is omnipresent in Samuel Beckett's *Molloy* for instance: "Unless you'd like to try a real emetic, I said, as if nothing had happened. I'm tired, he said. You go and lie down, I said, I'll bring you something nice and light in bed, you'll have a little sleep and then we'll leave together. I drew him to me. What do you say to that? I said. He said to it, Yes, papa."[4] Yet, the analogy cannot go beyond a superficial resemblance whose mechanisms are totally distinct. While in Beckett the obsessive verb "said" is the sign of a conversational exchange, of a constant alternation of answers, in Dawn Raffel's novel it is the emblem of the monologue one-sidedly developed by all the participants in the act of communication. The four characters more or less endowed with a voice (the aunt, the sister, the child, and the father) engage in a mock conversation devoid of apparent meaning, in the style of Eugene Ionesco's absurd plays: "The child said something. 'What?' said the mother. Listen, the aunt said. What did I tell you? What did I just now say?" (25). The interrogative mode is contagiously pervasive. The obsessive question "What?" suggests less a desire to check the content of what the child has heard and understood, but rather the imperfect functioning of personal memory and understanding. The characters seem

---

4. Samuel Beckett, *Molloy. Malone Dies. The Unnamable* (London: John Calder, 1959), 120.

to constantly doubt their essential mental and psychological faculties (logic, memory, existence itself). Recurrent questions tend to verify the subject and object of certain actions, in an attempt to clarify identities and events: "Who is sleeping in the chair? Who is breathing on the pillow? What in the world has been spilling in the kitchen?" (54). Questions that might seem pointless or symptomatic of a pathological drive are constantly formulated; they are accompanied by simple answers and digressions, bearing no explicit relation to the initial question: "Was this house hers? This house was not hers. The window was shut" (19). No discursive continuity is visible, except in a certain number of the aunt's monologues (in the sections entitled "Blood of the Morning," "A Note About Volume," and "The Aunt Sweeps," for instance), where words flow in a coherent stream, with no dramatic interruptions.

In the face of the placid, but obstinate onslaught of domestic objects, questions related to property and possession are repeatedly asked: who is the owner of the house, with its plethoric and proliferating content? The house oscillates among possible owners and consequently loses any point of stable ownership: "Nothing is ours here" (104). The doubtful status of possession is heavily emphasized; neither the aunt, who has always been entombed inside the house, in the dreary intimacy of furniture and china, nor the sister, who chose to break loose and embark upon a life of exilic mobility, claims the maternal heritage: "What a nomad she was, well thumbed—this house not hers, this fan refreshing nothing" (28). The accumulation of unwieldy objects requires endless sessions of housekeeping, of conscientious, but inefficient scraping: "You'd think for the labor involved, you'd think it was mine, this house, and me the rightful mistress. It's Father's house. Rest assured, this isn't my house. No sirree. I dust too" (71). The idea of possession itself is endowed with spectral undertones, since it is often anchored in the past, not in the present: "This room was hers, had once been hers" (15). Possession is forsaken and is only evoked as a dreamy hypothesis, as an arbitrary possibility: "The place was not the aunt's. Suppose, for the sake of discussion, the place was the father's" (6). The novel thus blends both the heavy materiality of objects and the idea of naked dispossession, in a strange mixture of material accumulation and the total denial of possession. The house thus becomes the scene of a domestic dystopia, a place of no place, a place out of space and time, a place with no owner, nobody's place. The novel presents a cataclysmic still life of rottenness, a radical landscape of the vanity of vanities, a prelude to an apocalypse that promises to bring not only destruction, but also revelation (which is precisely the meaning of *apocalypse*), the revelation suggested by the final sentences of the novel.

Dispossession and the failure of communication are closely connected. Thus, in the sentence "Suppose, for the sake of discussion, the place was the father's" (6), the circumstances and conditions of dialogue are created, albeit without any convincing results. Communication among the various characters is condemned to stagnation, but a certain number of artifices of vitality manage to create the illusion of an ongoing verbal exchange. Among such artifices one finds not only a formula like "for the sake of discussion" (6), but also the constant use of imperatives whose addressee has no clear identity. Nobody answers, nobody performs any action when hearing these imperatives, but the reader is summoned, dragged into the story, and feels compelled to listen and to participate: "Why, look at the child, just look at the child!" (3), "I like a moment to myself, you know. Listen, what with all the commotion . . ." (43), "Look at my flesh. Just look at my flesh" (44). The dominant, obsessive imperative is that of listening: "Listen! Behold!" (56), "Listen, now. I do my best" (80). The aunt talks to herself or to the child, a posture that foreshadows the role of narrator she will play later on: "Listen. What did your mother go and do?" (27). The characters call out to an invisible or mute interlocutor (to themselves, possibly), asking for somebody's attention, developing an imperative tic, clinging to the phatic[5] function of language in order to systematically check that the communicative channels are open, even if no message ever seems to pass. The recurrent use of "listen" as a ritual formula helps establish a communicational link that is actually never materialized, which remains empty and meaningless, a formal tie that fails to bind. Centered around the code of communication and not on its content, the aunt's discourse is characterized by an inflation of the metalinguistic function: it attempts to find an interlocutor more than it attempts to transmit a semantic load.

Nevertheless, one can identify a case of successful dialogue, though extremely terse, in the short section entitled "Q & A,"

5. Roman Jakobson, *Essais de linguistique générale* (Paris: Éditions de Minuit, 1963), 215.

which, as the title indicates, consists of a precise question followed by a precise answer. The speakers' identities are not revealed: "*Q*. Was there really a gemstone hidden on the premises? *A*. Yes" (63). This brief section is an exceptional case of smooth, limpid communication, in the margin of the foggy main narrative, a lucid fragment whose status is unclear (as if an omniscient or omniclarifying entity had intervened to bring momentary relief and to testify to the existence of a "normal" dialogic register of the logos). The above quoted dialogue creates the illusion that other such exchanges might follow and progressively provide answers to an increasing number of accumulating questions.

While fruitful exchanges are absent from the text, monologues largely prevail. Discourses of solitude and introspection, monologues feature endlessly on many pages in unbroken typographic blocks. The absence of fractures is surprising, for the narrative environment surrounding the monologues is essentially broken and evasive, exhibiting a brittle quality of the words and plot falling apart. A certain lyrical impetus seems to animate words and to make them cohere effortlessly, harmoniously, in an exclamative, ecstatic mood: "Oh, blood of the morning, angel of breath!" (14), "She was a woman unmanned and moving to a bed. So many nights! Oh, wanderer!" (17). The sentences in the monologues are characterized by a rhythmic pattern, by a musical cadence, by a repetitive and alliterative euphony: "She stood at a window, too well touched, untouched, a rib, a rib, thwarted hoarder of increase, a bearer of ill-got fruit, of breath" (16). Several elements of the scenario of the fall are visible (the rib, the fruit, the woman as child-bearer), leading to the reappearance of the theme of Eden and of the loss of Eden introduced by the divine question "Where are you?" which opens the book. Dawn Raffel's meticulous linguistic work is perceptible in the play on assertion and negation ("touched, untouched"), in the laconic emphasis laid on "rib," in the internal rhyme of "thwarted" and "hoarder," in the phonetic similarities linking "bearer" and "breath." Sentences are sometimes brief, of a minimalist syntax, marked by alliteration and phonetic echoes, such as the plosive consonants in a phrase like "breasted, pierced and swabbed" (15). At such moments, Dawn Raffel's prose dangles above the abyss of poetry, displaying an eerie lyricism. All of the little boy's ancestors are visible in his physical traits, their features melt into his, in a concrete image of the hereditary weight introduced by the title.[6] In order to indicate the twofold nature of the boy's features (they are both his and his family's), the sentence is being done and undone, replete with corrections, retractions, added elements marking the hesitating quality of the genetic heritage: "Unquiet, the boy did sleep, in witnessed thrash, his hair (their hair) unruly, his brow (their brow) severe, the little nose's bridge a narrow one" (16). A wide range of negatively prefixed adjectives is used ("unquiet" or the adjectival couple "touched/untouched," quoted

6. Dawn Raffel comments on the body that is carried in the title: "The title, *Carrying the Body*, refers to the body of knowledge and feeling that we carry from one generation to the next. I believe that a good deal of our patterns of feeling, our ways of viewing life, and our ways of carrying our own bodies through the world are largely inherited, not entirely mindfully, from our parents and grandparents." (Dawn Raffel interviewed by Dina Di Maio, ibid.).

earlier). The negative markers are embedded in the morphology of words, suggesting a delayed beginning, the futility of objects, a general state of incompleteness. The negative prefix "un" signals the passage to a state of innocence or to a state of undeveloped larvae ("The lover slept, as if unborn," 67), the ruthless progress of disease ("ungenerous infection," 47), the inability to perform a given action ("she felt herself [. . .] wetted and heated — a bit lip besotted, unsuckleable," 47).

Inversion is a key device, leading to the delayed appearance of a word generally expected earlier in the sentence. The effect is that of a stately prose, in which gestures and speech are slow, hieratic, mysterious. Inversion affects all parts of speech, attributive elements ("All curve she was," 28, "a girl among the girls and disinherited ideas of girls she has been," 15), direct objects ("He too, the aunt thought, this restlessness inherited," 92) or possessive pronouns ("Mother of the aunt and of the mother of the child and of her own demise — swift passage, hers," 7). It seems that, in the contagious world of *Carrying the Body* (a sick, contaminated body), the body of language itself is poetically diseased, refusing to function according to some (neat, ideal, utopian) linguistic norm. Inversion may be seen as a "verbal plague, a contagious sickness in the world of words,"[7] spreading from one sentence to the other and conferring on the text a unity of style.

---

7. This is how Vladimir Nabokov described paronomasia in his novel *Bend Sinister*. Vladimir Nabokov, "Introduction," *Bend Sinister* (New York: Vintage, 1947), xv.

In the reified universe of the house, objects show unmistakable signs of animation and independence; they tend to shun the passive voice and to perform human actions. Objects have a pulse of their own, they are alive, active, alert: "Collars at attention awaited a neck" (7), "The darkness was active" (12). One is reminded of Gertrude Stein's *Tender Buttons* (1914), with its heavy emphasis on objects and materials associated with a variety of unexpected verbs. In the following example, even if the gesture is most likely performed by a human hand, a piece of furniture appears to be its agent, reminding one of fairy tales and oneiric visions: "The bed unmade itself" (48). Inanimate matter and the shriveled bodies of the characters change places. The reversal of the active and passive voice is visible in the behavior of the house, which opens up to discovery and vision ("A room opened up to her," 13), giving occasional signs of movement ("The room seemed to move to him," 66). Just as the boy is described as a creature made of jelly, his toy acquires eyes: "Jellied, the child rolled bread, chewed open-mouthed. At the foot of the chair was the toy. The toy had eyes" (8). The father is a lifeless dummy, who seldom finds a voice; his body is a protruding mass of bones, of hardened, sleepy flesh: "The father's bones rose out of the body" (6). The father's drowsy state dissimulates however latencies of speech and action. He is suspended on the brink of a discourse that is about to begin: "In a sweat in the chair, in recline, yet active, as if, the aunt thought, he could almost simply be roused into discourse" (56). The father is inseparable from and eventually indistinguishable from his chair: "'Pop,' said the mother, addressing the chair" (9). The body is essentially defined as matter, as a fusion of chemical substances, and this heavy material emphasis contaminates even the invisible, immaterial elements connected to the body, for example, breath: "The body is carbon, the breath is furred" (16). What causes the objects to find a new life? Decline, neglect, forgetfulness paradoxically ensure their renewal and rebirth, just like the renewal of grammatical habits: "Neglect had remade things" (19). Nouns designating objects and parts of the body are not the only lexical elements that show signs of lifelessness, but also adjectives, which, employed in unusual structures, perform all sorts of actions: "Quiet, the aunt thought, seemed to swell" (56). The beginning of the novel projects the reader into a universe of disease, where persons and things are equally sick, suffering from unknown and unknowable pathologies, which seem to find their source in the child ("infection . . . bred on the child," 3). The house is threatened by a palpable, contagious swarming of germs and bacteria, which spread and modify the aspect and constitution of objects; light is contaminated ("the festering light," 3) and so are the child's clothes and toy, which regress toward the vegetative existence of microscopic organisms: "fungal diapers," "a bulbous, sucked-on toy in the likeness of some sort of life-form" (3). The lethargic, sickly child in *Carrying the Body* reminds one of Ruby Lamar and Lee Goodwin's apathetic son in William Faulkner's *Sanctuary*, a child who never speaks, however, contrary to Dawn Raffel's Jim.

The hesitation between animate and inanimate ultimately leads to a state of acute indeterminacy: "Something escaped her" (12), "She was serving something. The table wobbled" (21). A general mood of indefiniteness sets in, as if, in their twilight cohabitation, human beings and objects had been mutually contaminated with the same decrepitude and inertia. The general absence of orientation, of purpose, affects human desires and designs, which lack coherence and consistency, being aimlessly dispersed in a hazy indefiniteness: "There was something desired—some warm thing" (61). This suspension of individual will is paradoxically accompanied by an expression of certainty rendered through the obsessive repetition of "of course." While opacity and meaninglessness dominate the narrative scene, sentences are often marked by this phrase, thus creating a contrastive effect: the foggy plot is cleared from time to time to make room for the sunny obviousness of "of course": "The aunt, of course, watched" (5), "'She's called the bride,' the aunt said, holding the bride for the child to see (but not, of course, touch) . . ." (26), "'Pop,' said the mother. 'Pop,' as if she were the child—which, of course, she was" (9). The repetition of "of course" seems mechanical in nature, amounting to an incontrollable verbal hiccup. The obviousness of acts and events is suggested; however, there is no genuine reason underlying it. When stumbling across "of course," the reader hesitates between the revelation of the unexpected and the predictable result, between the awakening of consciousness and the mere verbal tic.

The putrid material universe of the house is counterbalanced by a bloody elsewhere projected by the father's war stories of destruction and mutilation: "He liked to tell stories of where he had been, the country he'd come from, ashes now, of course, he'd say—burnt roads, shoes lost, a house passed by gone up in flames" (75). These narratives, no matter how abject and terrifying, are seen by the father as a form of escape: "Let me tell you a story of someplace else. Skies dark from smoke-stacks, a factory, a ruin of clay" (78). Trapped inside the house, the aunt finds only one way out: the window constantly open on to the surrounding world, on to the nearby railway station, which sends its melancholy sounds and black smoke inside the house itself. A dream of escape brightens up, for a moment, the bleakness of the aunt's solitary life: "She was waiting for it—the train; oh, come, I said!—and stood by the window and yearned for reckless exile" (111). As an echo to Anton Chekhov's provincial despair, the aunt imagines her own departure (a bitter departure, however, described in terms of exile), just like the three sisters who summon all of their energies in order to reach a privileged destination, a remote, idealized Moscow. Similarly, Elise, before leaving the house, had been haunted by the open windows and by the promises of escape offered by the train: "Forever at the window. Always at the window. Pressed to the window, waiting for it—the whistle in the night. [. . .] Someone was beckoning her in the night" (74–75).

The call of a world elsewhere and the desire for genuine

communication with a fellow human being seem to materialize in the aunt's relation with the child, her sister's son. The two characters are strongly connected by a bond of affection and by the verbal ties of intermittent conversations. These emotional and verbal links allow Dawn Raffel to explore the idiosyncrasies of childish speech and to create, at the end of the book, the haven of light and love mentioned by the author in the interview with Dina Di Maio. While the child learns to speak, the aunt learns to tell stories: these two activities are mirrored throughout the text. The child babbles random words he hears around him, jumbling them, whereas the aunt babbles various versions of *Three Little Pigs*, subjecting them to a gradual process of perverse degradation. The child's linguistic innocence matches the aunt's narrative euphoria, provoked and sustained by a bottle of gin, which the child also samples from time to time. The aunt is a drunken narrator, playing the part of a degenerate Scheherazade, who loses control of the narrative and starts using learned words, which are incomprehensible for her nephew. Gradually, the aunt constructs parallels between her own situation, the situation of her family, and the story of the three little pigs: "The mother of the pigs, of the first little pig and of the second little pig, and so forth, the heretofore indispensable mother was suffering distress, for they had broken her heart" (35). In each of his answers, the child naively repeats a single word he has managed to grasp: "Her hard? said the child" (35). The narrative slowly becomes a space of personal vengeance for the aunt, who drifts away from the well-known story into the domain of moral examples and caveats:

"Listen to me. That pig should not have left home in the first place" (42). This warning comes too late: the little pig has already left the house and the creative anger of the aunt cannot help him find the way leading back home.

Generally characterized by heaviness and fixity, the aunt awakes at the end of the novel, replacing inertia with a frantic dynamism, falling from the window "in gravity's bosom" (119) while still holding the child in her arms: "She leaped, or rather, fell, from the window holding the child, still holding the child, and felt her breasts pushed into her, felt her breasts against her ribs, as if they were bound there, pressed by the child, and held him, and stumbled in the dirt there . . ." (125). The last sentence of the novel associates gravity and grace in the epiphany of a fortunate fall, which allows the aunt and the child to share the tenderness of a mute embrace: "He opened his eyes, for a moment bright, as if he quite saw her, as if he quite knew her, and closed his eyes, and visibly trembled, chin tipped back, the breath released, as if in ecstasy, the aunt thought, as if, in fact, in love" (126). The quest pattern of *Carrying the Body* thus comes to light. The "ecstasy" expressed by the child's face and the recovery of a clear vision (arguably, in an act of recognition, he sees her and acknowledges their affective kinship) are signs of an accomplished quest. The word "ecstasy" refers to an abandonment of the stasis, to the discovery of a world elsewhere, beyond the ruined house. The apocalypse thus recovers its initial meaning, that of the revelation and the unveiling of a mystery, that of the gravity and grace of being, of a redeeming "love."

NOCTURNAL VARIATIONS: THE WRITING OF TRANSGRESSION IN *NIGHTWORK* BY CHRISTINE SCHUTT

CLAIRE FABRE-CLARK
Translated from the French by Claire Fabre-Clark

"In this description [of death by Milton] all is dark, uncertain, confused, terrible, and sublime to the last degree."

— *Edmund Burke*[1]

Christine Schutt's palette covers all possible degrees of shadow, from half-light to ink-black night in which dreamlike shifts and distortions operate. The exquisite terror which comes out from this

---

1. Edmund Burke *A Philosophical Enquiry into the Origins of Our Ideas of the Sublime and Beautiful* (1757; Oxford: Oxford University Press, 1990).

This essay originally appeared in French in the publication of a special issue (#38, June 2005) of *Les Cahiers Charles V*: "États-Unis: formes récentes de l'imagination littéraire (II: 'Recent American Letters')," resulting from the research work conducted at the Observatoire de Littérature Américaine (Paris 7-Denis Diderot) under the direction of Marc Chenétier, Professor of American Literature, Institut Universitaire de France, editor of this collection of essays.

gloom recalls the Sublime as defined by Edmund Burke as well as, in some of its tones, Gothic literature. But the main intention here is by no means to present Christine Schutt as a Gothic writer. Taking the title literally, we will instead see how the night "works" the writing to produce poetic forms situated in the complicated zones of desire, at the outmost bounds of fantasy and memory.

BORDERS

In *Nightwork* we experience a sudden brutal and total immersion. The incipits of the stories rely on a certain number of presuppositions or reconstructions furnished by the reader to render the text intelligible. Schutt regularly exploits this possibility, repeating it in many different ways.

First, these texts often impose fait accompli upon us, forcing us to rapidly accept situations that are marked with transgression. From one story to another, all the possible combinations of family relationships, and their associated perversions (incest and/or violence), are recited: a daughter with her father in a car in "You Drive," a mother with her son in "What Have You Been Doing?" a student and her professor in "Teachers," a girl, her father, and her grandfather in "The Enchantment." Even when it is not a question of incestuous relationships as such, the boundaries are progressively blurred between generations in "Good Night Sweetheart," between the living and the dead in "Dead Men," and between the living and the dying in "Daywork," "Metropolis," and "Giovanni and Giovanna."

From the first lines, the relations that are outlined between characters suggest that the overstepping of the limit has already taken place, that the incestuous disorder has been present for quite some time, as if it had become part of everyday life. The shock felt by the reader is all the greater owing to the apparent banality of the situation, which seems almost normal to the characters, as at the beginning of "What Have You Been Doing?":

> She was out of <u>practice</u>, and he wanted <u>practice</u>, so they started <u>kissing</u> each other, and they called it <u>practicing</u>, this <u>kissing</u> that occurred to him. In the middle of rooms, she obliged, in her bedroom, his bedroom, a <u>kissing</u> done standing, her hands on his shoulders, his not quite on her waist, heads tilted, mouths open. Like this? the boy asked, and the mother said "Yes," but kept her tongue to herself, and only laughed sometimes at the suddenness of his — his tongue that in its darting seemed not his. (31, my underlining)

The reader easily understands the first pieces of information in the text: this is undoubtedly a man and a woman, whose complementary nature is playfully underlined by the initial symmetry: "She was out of practice, and he wanted practice." There is a certain lightness in the tone of these opening lines, which makes the kiss something of a mutual agreement of no particular importance. This effect is reinforced by the repetition of the words "practice" and "kissing," whose grammatical status develops quickly from the present participle, to substantivized verb and finally, to countable noun. The identity of the protagonists, whose simple designation by the personal pronouns "she" and "he" is sufficient to satisfy the reader. However, at the appearance of "the boy" and "the mother," the reader is obliged to take account of this new information, provided almost in passing. Our reading of the remainder of the text is therefore conditional on this mixing of modes, which the story plays with from the opening and which serves to normalize a transgressive situation. Adding to this disquiet, the impression of reciprocity between mother and son makes the origin of this desire difficult to pin down: on a number of occasions, the mother attempts to reimpose the limits by restraining her son's passion, not entirely convincingly:

> She was in the bathroom, and he was at the door. Mornings, evenings. "Do you mind?" she answered. "Are you deaf?" she asked, pressing a wet washcloth over her breasts and turning away from the cold huff of air in the door's opening. "Just checking," the boy said — and the mother smiled when she shouted, "I have no privacy here!" (33, my underlining)

The expression "the door's opening" illustrates well the motif of transgression present across all of the text. This denotes the barrier that is impossible to respect between the bodies of the mother and the son. Further, "opening" takes on a sexual connotation emphasized by the potential personification of the door through the possessive form. This erotization continues in the following passage referring to the depth of the partition between the two bedrooms: "divisions so thin she could hear the boy at night butting against the wall between her bedroom and his" (33, my underlining).

The diegetic barriers (doors, landings, divisions) have thus either already been breached or act as porous invitations to passage. Entry into Schutt's text thus implies facing the complexity of flows, of unnatural and unexpected exchanges. By imagining the reciprocity of relations, Schutt calls into question stereotypical divisions, in particular between victims and tormentors.

The story "Dead Men" illustrates the disruption of categories in more ways than one. It first proposes a grotesque metaphor for this intermediary space, which Schutt so often appeals to in her writing, by presenting a woman in the act of making love to a (live) man above another (dead) man who is wrapped up under the bed: the macabre content of this scene is counterbalanced by the comic effects of the lexical and syntactical choices: "There is a man on top of her up on the top of the bed, and there is a man under her down under the bed, but the man down there is dead" (51). The complexity of this sentence results from the reduction of the lexicon to a bare minimum of monosyllabic or disyllabic terms alternating between prepositions (on, of) and adverbial fragments (up, down). The symmetrical layout produces a syncopated rhythm: "on top of her up on the top of the bed" and "under her down under the bed" that echo each other in the same way as the simple words of a child's rhyme. As in the incipit of "What Have You Been Doing?" the reader is immediately caught up in the whirlwind of translation, and savors the syntactical and rhythmic richness before understanding its meaning.

The story then unfolds by following the association of ideas that come to the narrator while she is making love. Evocations of lovemaking with her (living) lover and memories of previous scenes, whether real or imagined we do not know, with the body under the bed, as well as her previous life with the dead man (while he was still alive) are all jumbled up. The slippage between the different tenses and the confusion regarding their degree of reality for the narrator are sustained by the expression "the dead man," which designates the other man even when she remembers him still alive: "She watched — she watched the dead man clip his nails into last night's coffee and found bleedy streaks on his pillow [...]" (53). The literal repetition of the first designation ("the dead man") (rather than the use of a pronoun, for example) gives the named person a surreal character, as a dead man becomes the agent of an action. The strangeness of the situation, intensified by the syntax, rises in a crescendo only to finish in a sudden collapse when the (live) lover cannot satisfy the masochistic desires of the woman as well as the dead lover once did. This story could easily be interpreted allegorically as the weight of the past and the impossibility of leaving it behind.

The middle ground between life and death reappears as the source of climactic joy and pain in "Metropolis," but without the grotesque dimension. The narrator speaks of her suffering with a man whose dying takes an age: she only calls him "the dying man" (which we recognize as a variation on the "dead man" cited above), as if the moment of passage was frozen for an unbearable eternity. The signifiers for night and darkness peak in intensity in "Metropolis": "the windows <u>darken</u> suddenly in our apartment" (79), "the <u>night</u> tipping shut, a lid" (79), "somewhere <u>obscured</u> in this <u>obscuring</u> city" (79), "strangely <u>inky</u> evenings" (79), "a <u>dark</u> bed" (82), "combed <u>black</u> dirt" (82), "the dying man has called out for his mother in the middle of the *night*" (82), "but that there is the <u>night</u> to be got through" (83), and "sleepless <u>night</u>" (83, my underlining). Apart from "middle of the night" and "sleepless night," which are well-worn phrases, all of the other terms denoting shadow and darkness are used in metaphorical expressions. As is often the case in Gothic American writing, fear is itself mentioned explicitly by the narrator in the middle of her story: "<u>Here's scary</u> — a man downstairs in a small light drinking — and a woman just above him, waiting in a dark bed." (82, my underlining).

The defamiliarization provoked by transgression is seen both in the figurative games and in the narrative description. The narrators do, indeed, sometimes seem to realize that their lives are not the same as those of others, that they live in a fringe area, different from the rest of the world. In "The Summer After Barbara Claffey," we first notice the contrast between the mother-daughter couple and the others, and then the daughter's feeling of exclusion when her mother meets a new lover. "Mother says, 'Our house marks the start of this corny town,' and the two of us laugh at what it takes to be the start of something" (19). For the mother and the daughter, others are seen as people who are both radically different and indistinguishable, intruders or invaders, to the extent that their surnames act as collective nouns: "The Smiths across the street, the Dunphies next door, all the way to the end of the road — in what Mother calls a farm and Barbara

Claffey calls a subdivision—are neighbors dressed in scant disguises" (22). This elision between a proper and a collective noun becomes more pronounced with the pluralization of the names of her mother's lovers. These spoilsports are all indiscriminately called Jack: "I do not have the face my mother wears for all her <u>Jacks</u> [. . .] Beautiful, the <u>Jacks</u> all say, and she is" (26, my underlining). In the end the reader gets lost in the subtle designations that mix the different values of the determiners between "this new Jack" (the new lover), "this last Jack" (the previous one), and "that Jack" (an even older one). These syntactical twists make up for the girl's lack of expression. We find the same plurality of first names with the double effect of otherness and interchangeability in "You Drive," when the father and daughter look out of the car at the lights coming on in the houses:

> So she drove again, and she told her father what it was as they passed it, and in what connection to him were these women at the end of narrow drives in houses near the water. She spoke of <u>aproned Annes and pretty Susies</u>. "You knew them," she told her father.
>
> Her father said, "Did I?"
>
> Her father said, "I don't miss many people." (15, my underlining)

The transformation of proper noun into collective noun is here based not only on the pluralization of first names but also on the introduction of the adjectives "aproned" and "pretty."

Even when they do not feel cut off from others, the characters may sometimes express the feeling of no longer being at home in their own body, as suggested by the recurring metaphor of the body as an ill-fitting piece of clothing: as in the case of the two girls waiting their turn to be "educated" by the narrator's father-in-law: "how we used to stand in line for it, me and Barbara Claffey, shivering in our new bodies and waiting our turn for instruction" ("The Summer After Barbara Claffey" [21]), or the mother after her son's kiss: "in the middle of a room she did not recognize, in a body that was suddenly not quite hers" ("What Have You Been Doing?" [35]).

THE UNNAMABLE

The sentiment of defamiliarization comes up in all the strategies that tend to blur the referent in these stories. As in a number of other stories in this collection where the narrators or characters attempt to bring back a past traumatic experience ("The Summer After Barbara Claffey," "Religion," "The Enchantment"), the central referent stays in the shadows of the text and the story is built up hesitantly, from scraps that are not easy to put together. Thus, the denotative dimension always remains in the background, as if struck by suppression. Indeterminacy and polysemy colonize the text in the form of an abundance of indefinite pronouns ("it," "that") or of semantically vague generic terms ("thing," "something") to the extent of obscuring the identity and the stability of the referent. It goes without saying that the sexual connotations of terms like "it" and "thing" often point the reader toward interpretations of the unspoken, while a second reading often shows that the referent remains opaque.

In "The Enchantment," the anecdotal story is impossible to resume as the fragmented prose only yields splinters, shards of a mirror in which the image of the narrator can barely be picked out. Battling with the infinite puzzle of her own memory, she expresses above all loss and confusion. The writing, by which the young girl wishes to piece together the facts of her own past — with an obviously schizophrenic father and a seductive authoritarian grandfather — only makes matters even murkier, for which she finally excuses herself: "I'm sorry, I get confused" (67). The reader must listen carefully to various echoes created by the text, which is the only way of reconstructing any meaning. We stop, for example, at the evocation of Sunday dinner at the grandfather's: "all those Sunday dinners with the slavering roast <u>sliced bloody</u> on the tines of the carving tools" (71). The choice of phrasing is typical of Schutt's writing: the subject is so dense that two words (a past participle and an adjective) suffice to create a strong image summarizing a whole series of actions. Moreover, the highlighting of the adjective "bloody" can be interpreted as the expression of the fascination common to all children for the blood of the Sunday roast. This detail is then reinterpreted retrospectively as a metonymic displacement of an aggressive gesture of the girl toward her father found at the end of the story: "Then I was using something sharp on him, just to draw a little blood" (78).

In "You Drive," a story delivered as fragments materialized by disjointed paragraphs, the incipit blurs together incest (and, more generally, sex), drugs, and violence:

> She brought him <u>what</u> she had promised, and they did <u>it</u> in his car, on the top of the car park, looking down onto the black roofs of buildings, and she said, <u>or she thought she said</u>, "I like your skin," when what she really liked was the color of her father's skin, the mottled white of his arms and the clay color at the roots of the hairs along his arms. (3, my underlining)

The indefinite pronoun "it," refers to an expression, which is itself indeterminate—"what she had brought." As a result of the polysemy of the verb "do," the phrase could just as well refer to sexual relations as the drugs that the young protagonist seems to share with her father. Whether it is a question of selling drugs or promiscuity, in which both mother and daughter partake, or sexual relations between the father and his daughter, the confusion between these taboo referents is maintained throughout the text. Referents are constantly obscured by indeterminacy. This indeterminacy extends itself in Schutt's use of the word "blow" in all its acceptations (violence, drugs, and/or disappointment) in the story's last line—"Arms crossed and eyes shut tight in the cold of the car, she moved a little closer to him and waited for the blow" (17). When the car—an accessory to "passage" par excellence—sets off it is to go to an indeterminate place, a sort of building site exemplified by emptiness "[. . .] he drove her to an <u>unfinished place</u> and pointed. 'I have <u>something</u> to do with <u>that.</u>' She saw a building, girders, rags, nets, menacing <u>vacancies</u>" (9). The form of the juxtaposed fragments chosen for the story's narration creates a discontinuity that further obscures the referent. Between fantasy and memory, perception and daydream ("and she said, <u>or she thought</u> she said"), the text oscillates constantly, as if to hold back the unbearable, the unnamable. The fragments, debris, and scraps that litter the floor certainly reflect the abject, but they are also the last traces that the writing brings together as best it can. In the middle of these fragments and this debris often lurks something indescribable and appalling, like the bastard object that the young girl finds in the fange of the garden:

> "Garbage, then," I say, like all my other finds — an upper plate of teeth, scarves, umbrellas, pens, and once, in the middle of the driveway, a ruined shirt so flattened by the weight of cars driving over and over, it had taken the shape of a dead thing, and I had carried it to Mother on a stick. ("The Summer After Barbara Claffey," 20)

Countering these shadowlands where the referent is uncertain are visions where details are magnified. Often the gaze concentrates on a part of the body — the skin or the mouth — which becomes for a while an object of fascination. The white of the father's skin in "You Drive" becomes a surface on which the young girl's desire writes itself: "the mottled white of his arms and the clay color at the roots of the hairs along his arms." Listening carefully, there are three principal accents that appear in this phrase referring to the "mottled," "clay," and "roots." The lyrical density of this sentence eroticizes the skin of the father as seen by his daughter. The conjunction of strong melodic accents and of semantic and phonic wealth is also one of the characteristics of Schutt's writing, which naturally creates tension when opposed to hesitation and indeterminacy.

THE BODY AND ITS TRACES

Many other examples can serve to illustrate the lexical and syntactic compactness of Schutt's prose. This richness, unfurled at each line, contributes to the isotopy of orality in which bodily and verbal violence are mixed, the pleasure of words and the dream of consumption. In "Good Night Sweetheart" we seem to clearly hear the voice of the author commenting on her own work:

> He takes me to dinner; he lets me talk and talk, like boys used to do. My mouth waters with the pleasure of it, telling stories whole, being heard; I order dessert; I flirt. All this heat hatches my face. I feel it, and I am happy, schoolgirl happy, with a man I am afraid to kiss. (37)

In general, the narrators and the characters are always sorely tempted to taste others—"Your mouth went to it" (99)—to drink them—"My son's wet mouth, I could drink from it still" (81)—to lick them—"Under the kitchen table, I licked this Jack's shoes, both. But neither tasted of anything I knew of" (24)—or just to simply devour them—like the gerbils that eat each other in "To Have and To Hold." The pleasure of orality is indissociable from the insatiability of the (female) characters, from the abyssal and constitutive lack of their being: "— me, a hole, a gap, a breach, a space, an absence and longing" ("The Enchantment," 78). In *Pouvoirs de l'horreur*, Julia Kristeva evokes this conjunction between oral linguistic activity and dreams of devouring: «Par la bouche que je remplis de mots plutôt que de ma mère qui me manque désormais plus que jamais, j'élabore ce manque et l'agressivité qu l'accompagne, en *disant*. [. . .] Mais on est en droit de supposer que toute activité de verbalisation, qu'elle nomme ou non un objet phobique ayant trait à l'oralité, est une tentative d'introjecter les incorporats.»[2] ("Through my mouth, which I fill in with words rather than with my mother, I elaborate this lack and the aggression that accompanies it, by saying. [. . .] But one may suppose that any form of verbalization, whether or not it names a phobic object, is an attempt at introjecting the incorporate," my translation.)

The loss of a mother is at the heart of the story "Daywork." The story opens with the scene of the narrator and her sister cleaning out their mother's attic while she is in the hospital in the final stages of her illness. The attic is described by the oxymoron "<u>awful heaven</u>," a phrase that immediately recalls the "concatenation of rapture and awe"[3] which is a property of the Sublime emotion according to Burke. The two young women suddenly find themselves faced with all the artificial limbs and medical accessories of

<hr />

2. Julia Kristeva, *Pouvoirs de l'horreur* (Paris: Le Seuil, 1980), 52.

3. This expression comes from Florian Tréguer, "L'evénement et l'éventualite: les Formes du sublime dans l'œuvre de Don DeLillo" in *Revue Française d'Etudes Américaines*. (*Le sublime en question*, ed. Anne Battesti), no. 99 (February 2004), 56.

their dying mother: "Here they are tilted against the attic walls: the legs, the arms, the clamshell she wore instead of a spine. Here is some of Mother leaned up in the attic" (57), which have both reduced their mother to the rank of an object ("some of Mother") and acquired a kind of autonomous life on their own: "these parts of Mother that seem a part of her still, quite alive and listening in on what we talk about" (59). It is difficult not to think of Edgar Allan Poe's story "The Man That Was Used Up," as Schutt takes and transposes the grotesque and macabre motif of an artificial body whose limbs are both alive and dead.

While always dismembered to this degree, the body in Schutt's fiction is often tortured and bruised. It is not so much the theme of death that interests Schutt, but that of agony — "What else but love and God and dying?" in "Because I Could Not Stop for Death" (111) — the anguish from the ephemeral coexistence of life and death. But the moment of the final passage is also when the body may leave its final mark:

> Everything in the bedroom is purely itself, doorknobs, windows, dishes of loose change — and I am afraid. I am afraid the dying man will always be here, picking at his scabs, sniffing at his farts, wiping at his face with his day's dress shirt, leaving smudge and oil and threaded juices of himself on what surfaces he passes as he goes about his dying. ("Metropolis," 84)

The interlacing pools of bodily fluids ("threaded juices of himself") form a motif that is found in "Giovanni and Giovanna" and "Dead Men." This naturally partakes in the metatextual metaphor that represents the skin of the world (human skin, or the surface of objects) as a blank page and the mouth as an organ of verbal pleasure and extreme suffering: "from the sore that was her mouth," in "Teachers" (99). These descriptions present the advent of a trace that is not to be found before the sign, in its anteriority, but afterward, at the very instant which precedes the catastrophe. Far from grandiloquence, the debris and fragments associated with the body take their place in the collection of signs and designate metonynically the imminence of loss: "The bath towels, old messages, Q-tips, hair, the strewn ephemera of indoor living," in "Teachers" (106). The opposition of black and white, upon which the metatextual reading of the text is based, is not a clear antithesis involving absolute values. The figures of the night ("strangely inky evenings") are often written on unnameable backdrops (on "old-teeth yellow"), but these traces themselves are liable to fade away: "I white out trails of water leaking from her snarled hair," in "The Summer After Barbara Claffey" (25); or "his age bleaches even his past" in "Good Night Sweetheart" (39). As a counterpoint, the body also serves as a vehicle in many of the metaphors used to describe the world, even if the end result is fairly depressing: "Slip, panties, pearls, and dress, all the whites turned old-teeth yellow," in "The Summer After Barbara Claffey" (26) or "we watched for winter birds — blood smears in the trees" in "The Enchantment" (78).

It would therefore seem that in Christine Schutt's *Nightwork*, the expression of an insatiable and formless desire can only succeed via the transgression of the body and of codes. The analysis of detail has shown that Schutt often chooses a very dense syntax, preferring the "thematic" over the "rhematic"[4] and often plays on elisions or ellipses, even when these are not welcomed by established grammar. In Schutt's fiction, the circuits via which sense is established are often short-circuited, as illustrated by the huge compound nouns or the abundance of intricate sentences. The forms that she creates thus foster a troubled relationship with the notion of norm, which only persists in the background, like a vague shadow. The reader's certitudes wobble just as those of the young woman in "You Drive" who asks her father: "Should I be ashamed?"—to which he replies, in lieu of closure: "of what?"

4. A distinction made by enunciative linguistics between "rhematic" elements mentioned for the first time, and "thematic" ones, implicitly commented on.

Amfreville, Marc. "Le Sublime ou les ambiguïté." *Revue Française d'Etudes Américaines.* (*Le sublime en question*, ed. Anne Battesti), no. 99 (February 2004). Paris: Editions Belin.

Barth, John. *The Floating Opera* (1955). New York: Bantam Books, 1972.

Burke Edmund. *A Philosophical Enquiry into the Origins of Our Ideas of the Sublime and Beautiful* (1757). Oxford: Oxford University Press, 1990.

Kristeva Julia, *Pouvoirs de l'horreur*, Paris: Le Seuil, 1980.

Schutt, Christine. *Nightwork* (1996). Champaign, IL: Dalkey Archive Press, 2000.

Tréguer, Florian. "L'evénement et l'éventualite: les Formes du sublime dans l'oeuvre de Don DeLillo." *Revue Française d'Etudes Américaines.* (*Le sublime en question*, ed. Anne Battesti), no. 99 (February 2004). Paris: Editions Belin.

Kim Chinquee's collection *Oh Baby* will be published in 2008 by Ravenna Press. She teaches creative writing at Central Michigan University.

Lydia Davis, a 2003 MacArthur Fellow, is the author of, most recently, the story collection *Varieties of Disturbance* (Farrar, Straus & Giroux, 2007). Her most recent translation is *Swann's Way* by Marcel Proust (Viking Penguin, 2003), and she is currently translating *Madame Bovary* by Gustave Flaubert. She is on leave from SUNY Albany and is a fellow of the New York State Writers Institute.

Claire Fabre-Clark is a *maître de conférences*, a teaching and research position, at the University of Paris 12, France. She wrote her PhD on the poetics of the banal in Raymond Carver's short stories and has published articles on David Foster Wallace, Grace Paley, Nicholson Baker, and Patricia Eakins.

Augusta Gross is a frequent contributor to *NOON*. Her piano music was recorded recently by Bruce Levingston on a CD entitled *Reflections on Air*. She is currently collaborating on an upcoming CD with jazz pianist Janice Friedman.

Bill Hayward is a photographer and filmmaker who lives and works in New York City and Montana. The photographs featured are from Hayward's *Unexpected Truths* — a forthcoming book and traveling exhibition. Hayward's film *heartAttack* is scheduled for release in 2008. The book can be followed at unexpectedtruths. com, the film at reddressfilms.com

Brandon Hobson's book of short prose, *The Levitationist*, is available from Ravenna Press, originally published by Triple Press. His work has also appeared in *Narrative Magazine*, *elimae*, *Mad Hatters' Review*, and elsewhere online. He teaches English in Oklahoma City.

Tao Lin is the author of two collections of poetry, *Cognitive-Behavior Therapy* (Melville House, 2008), and *You Are a Little Bit Happier Than I Am* (Action Books, 2006). He is also the author of a novel, *Eeeee Eee Eeee* (Melville House, 2007) and a story collection, *Bed* (Melville House, 2007). His Web site is called *Reader of Depressing Books* and he lives in New York City.

Monica Manolescu-Oancea completed her PhD dissertation on Vladimir Nabokov at the University of Paris 7–Denis Diderot in 2005. She is a Lecturer at the English department of the University of Strasbourg. Her areas of teaching and research are American art and literature. She has written articles on Vladimir Nabokov, Rikki Ducornet, Edith Wharton, Steven Millhauser, and Dawn Raffel. She is currently working on a study of Vladimir Nabokov's geographies.

Clancy Martin, a Canadian, is Assistant Professor of Philosophy at the University of Missouri in Kansas City, and a frequent contributor to *NOON*. "This Is How I Got My Start in the Jewelry Business" is an excerpt from his novel *How to Sell*, forthcoming from Farrar, Straus & Giroux.

Laurence C. Peacock was born in Oneida County, New York, in 1927. "After graduating from high school, in Camden, I enlisted in the United States Navy. Later, I was employed in railroad service until appointed to the position of county civil defense director in the late 1960s. Moving south in 1982, I was employed as a front-desk supervisor in a motel. Later, I became employed as an administrative assistant in a South Carolina nursing home. After my wife died in 2002, I moved back north. I currently reside alone in Castorland, New York."

Dawn Raffel is the author of a novel, *Carrying the Body*, and a story collection, *In the Year of Long Division*. She is completing a new collection.

Deb Olin Unferth is the author of *Minor Robberies* (McSweeney's, 2007). Her fiction has appeared in *Harper's Magazine*, *Conjunctions*, *NOON*, *Fence*, the Pushcart Prize anthologies, and elsewhere.

THE EDITORS WISH TO THANK THE FOLLOWING
INDIVIDUALS FOR THEIR GENEROUS SUPPORT OF NOON:

Anonymous

Anonymous

Katie Baldwin

The Balsamo Family Foundation

Margaret Barrett

Francis and Prudence Beidler

Marcy Brownson and Edwin J. Wesely

Lisa Bornstein

Melinda Davis and Ealan Wingate

Lawrie and Tony Dean

Joseph Glossberg

Diane Holsenbeck

Ellen Kern

Christina Kirk

Laura S. Kirk

Lucy and Kenneth Lehman

Ruth and Irving Malin

Clancy Martin

Melanie Niemiec

Nuveen Investments

Thea and David Obstler

Lily Tuck

Abby S. Weintraub

Paul C. Williams

A NOTE ON THE TYPE

This book was set in Fournier, a typeface named for Pierre Simon Fournier, a celebrated type designer in eighteenth-century France. Fournier's type is considered transitional in that it drew its inspiration from the old style yet was ingeniously innovative, providing for an elegant yet legible appearance. For some time after his death in 1768, Fournier was remembered primarily as the author of a famous manual of typography and as a pioneer of the print system. However, in 1925 his reputation was enhanced when the Monotype Corporation of London revived Fournier's roman and italic.

Typeset by Matt Mayerchak, Needham, Massachusetts
Printed by Thames Printing Company, Inc.
Cover design by Susan Carroll

ONE HUNDRED AND FORTY-FIVE
STORIES IN A SMALL BOX

HARD TO ADMIT AND HARDER TO ESCAPE
BY SARAH MANGUSO

HOW THE WATER FEELS TO THE FISHES
BY DAVE EGGERS

MINOR ROBBERIES
BY DEB OLIN UNFERTH

THREE BOOKS OF SHORT-SHORT STORIES
ONE SLIPCASE COATED IN BEARS AND GOLD
OUT NOW FROM MCSWEENEY'S
STORE.MCSWEENEYS.NET

DALKEY ARCHIVE PRESS

Scandinavian Literature Series

The Parson's Widow

Marja-Liisa Vartio
Translation by Aili and Austin Flint

"There is something farcical about the smallness of the characters' world view, but there's a rigorous sort of honesty in
Vartio's approach, too: The bickering of Adele and Alma represents alienation as it is experienced by the average citizen
of the Western world in a way that the abstract nihilism of
Waiting for Godot and *No Exit* do not. Despair in miniature."
— *Kirkus*

978-1-56478-483-4 | $13.95 | Paperback

A Fool's Paradise

Anita Konkka
Translation by A.D. Haun and Owen Witesman

"[A]n elliptical novel of alienation and marginalisation
. . . It is kind of existential, but in a gentle way. Very little
of note happens, and the novel drifts around. Sometimes
sharp and funny, often poignant, and more than a little
strange, it is on the edge of surrealism but perhaps more
interested in the fact that, as the narrator says, 'there are a
lot of things in this world that can't be explained.'"
— Jerome de Groot, *The Guardian*

978-1-56478-422-3 | $12.95 | Paperback

Dark Paradise

Rosa Liksom
Translation by David McDuff

A man murders a grocer over fifteen cents—but in the
sharp, icy prose and detached tone that defines this collection, his crime seems neither sensational nor entirely
reprehensible. Liksom populates snow-covered landscapes,
antiseptic apartments, fish factories, and lumber camps
with the obsessive, the violent, and the unhinged. Yet the
lives and actions of these characters are infused with an
emotional intimacy that draws the reader into uncomfortable empathy with the extremity of their deeds.

978-1-56478-437-7 | $12.50 | Paperback

Oh Baby

flash fictions by Pushcart Prize-winning

Kim Chinquee

"Chinquee's stories explore the jangling nervous system beneath the ordinary surface of the world, and all the irony, shock, sadness, and hope contained therein." —*Jean Thompson*

Trade Paperback
ISBN: 978-0-9791921-8-0 * $13.95

Available directly from Ravenna Press
(www.ravennapress.com)
and from fine booksellers everywhere

Blue Tree
1283 Madison Ave.
212-369-2583

TALES OF LOVE AND MONEY

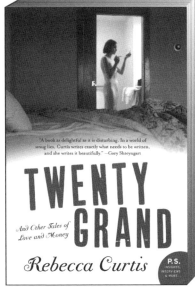

"A book as delightful as it is disturbing. In a world of smug lies, Curtis writes exactly what needs to be written, and she writes it beautifully." —Gary Shteyngart

TWENTY GRAND

And Other Tales of Love and Money

Rebecca Curtis

P.S. INSIGHTS, INTERVIEWS & MORE!

"A book as delightful as it is disturbing. In a world of smug lies, Curtis writes exactly what needs to be written, and she writes it beautifully."
—**Gary Shteyngart, author of *Absurdistan***

"Gorgeous. . . . Vivid imagery suffused with longing."
—***Los Angeles Times***

"Terrific. . . . Highly compelling. . . . If you're interested in the strangeness and sorrow of life, you'll find much to admire in *Twenty Grand.*"
—**Curtis Sittenfeld, *New York Times Book Review***

"Marvelous, inventive. . . . The writing soars."
—***San Francisco Chronicle***

HARPER ● PERENNIAL

Why the
Devil Chose
New England
for His Work

Stories by
Jason
Brown

"Stories so beautiful, faceted,
and durable, they feel excavated from
a mine. A collection of subtle gems."
—Aimee Bender

"Linked, gem-cut stories of troubled youths, alcoholics, illicit romances, the
burden of inheritance, and the bane of class, all set in the dense upper
reaches of Maine . . . delivered with hope, heart, and quiet humor."
      —*Elle*

OPEN CITY BOOKS
www.opencity.org

DIANE WILLIAMS

"Harnesses Williams's essentially comic sensibility to highly sophisticated, highly satisfying ends....(Her) irony never feels forced or distancing; instead, it allows her to get into some very messy facets of human desire as it gets rammed through American life." —*PUBLISHERS WEEKLY*

IT WAS LIKE MY TRYING TO HAVE A TENDER-HEARTED NATURE

A NOVELLA AND STORIES

"...the foremost advocate of flash fiction."
—*KIRKUS REVIEWS*

"... a master spy, a double agent in the house of fiction."
—*THE NEW YORK TIMES*

"One of the true living heroes of the American avant-garde." —JONATHAN FRANZEN

FC2
The University of Alabama Press
Tuscaloosa, Alabama 35487-0380
http://fc2.org